MATERNITY

The Complete Guide

DEE NEESON

MATERNITY SERVICES IN IRELAND

The Complete Guide

Gill and Macmillan

7674

Published in Ireland by
Gill and Macmillan Ltd
Goldenbridge
Dublin 8
with associated companies in
Auckland, Dallas, Delhi, Hong Kong,
Johannesburg, Lagos, London, Manzini,
Melbourne, Nairobi, New York, Singapore,
Tokyo, Washington.
© Dee Neeson 1986
5 4 3 2 1
0 7171 1469 4

Print origination in Ireland by Printset & Design Limited,
Dublin.
Printed in Great Britain by
Richard Clay (The Chaucer Press) Ltd, Bungay, Suffolk.

Contents

Introduction

This book is not about the physical side of pregnancy and childbirth — there are plenty such volumes available already, and the course of pregnancy does not alter all that much whether you are in Bantry or Birmingham, Limerick or London. I have therefore assumed in my writing that you will be using one of these titles as a reference to your changing body and to inform yourself about the physical aspects of birth and afterwards. Instead, this book aims to help you through what I would call the practical side of becoming a mother — from having a pregnancy test to claiming the children's allowance, and I have tried to cover all this specifically in the Irish context.

I decided to write this book for two reasons which are inter-connected. Having had to struggle to find out such information myself when I was pregnant for the first time, I wished that it had been available for me then. Later, after I had my second baby in circumstances which made it a really positive and happy event, I became involved in working with a couple of voluntary groups in the area of the maternity services, and in this way have had access to a large number of comments from women all over the country about their experiences. It became obvious that many women were, and still are, unable to find the information they need and so had to resort to a few crumbs of advice from friends, relations and odd paragraphs in books here and there. This book is therefore an attempt to remedy that situation and provide advice about maternity units, choices in childbirth, education for birth and so on.

I would, however, like to say that while I have made this book as practical and informative as possible, I could not and purposely have not included absolutely everything — there are some circumstances and situations which would require so much space to write about that the book would have become unwieldy, and I would therefore ask you also to use it as a source for other information. There are a number of groups dealing with special circumstances (the different kinds of physical handicap, for example) and so, if you want to find out more about a particular area mentioned in the text, I have listed relevant contacts at the end of each section or chapter.

It should be noted that unless otherwise stated, all the advice and information in this book refers to a normal, healthy pregnancy, delivery and post-partum period. Occasionally circumstances may arise which would alter what is stated here, but except in an absolute emergency this would, hopefully, be explained to you.

You should also note the terminology that I've used in the book. The word "doctor" refers to any doctor that you may meet in the course of your hospital visits, while "obstetrician" is used solely to represent a doctor of consultant level. The family doctor is referred to by the term "GP". Incidentally, a pet hate of mine is the misuse of "gynaecologist" for "obstetrician". While in practice they are usually the same person, a gynaecologist specialises in the treatment of female disorders and diseases, while an obstetrician deals with the events of pregnancy and birth, so in the context of this book "obstetrician" is the correct term.

I have had to refer to mothers and expectant mothers as "patients". I dislike this term in the context of maternity care, because the majority of pregnant women are perfectly healthy and not sick at all, as the word implies. I've been searching for a suitable word for a long time — I don't think "consumer" is quite right either — so if anyone has a good idea, please let me know!

I have referred to all the doctors and babies as "he", simply to save writing "s/he" and "his or her" each time it was necessary. It in no way reflects on the female sex — two of my children are girls and both my GP and my obstetrician are women — but was done for the sake of brevity and clarity.

Lastly, I am quite aware that some women may say that I have not been critical enough of the maternity services. I did not set out with the intention of writing a criticism of the maternity services, but rather to provide information and although I point out shortcomings I am not anti-doctor. My personal view is that whenever possible co-operation between consumers and professionals is far better than aggression; I know perfectly well that this does not always happen, but it does not exclude another personal view that we, as health service consumers, often need to be more assertive in asking for what we want. It is fairly obvious to the most casual observer that some maternity hospitals are far ahead of others, not in terms of technology but in the choices they offer to mothers; we can help to speed up the process of improvement in the other units by being ready to state our needs and wishes. Admittedly we may not always succeed, but if enough women are prepared to think about what they want and to say so, then eventually our voices will have to be listened to.

Acknowledgments

So many people have helped me over the last few years that it would be impossible to acknowledge them all, and I would ask them to take this as my thanks to them. I would like to single out my friends in the Association for Improvements in the Maternity Services (AIMS) and the Irish Childbirth Trust (ICT) who have helped me in various ways, and to all those women who filled in the questionnaires for AIMS, extracts of which are used in this book. Special thanks are due to my good friend Aileen Henderick who was also my ante-natal teacher and who helped to make three of my births such good, positive experiences, and to Carmel Gilbride for all her relevant comments.

Thanks are also due to Dr. Paddy Ann MacBride-Freyne who helped me with the medical aspects of the book, and to Dr. Miriam Brennan of St. Columcille's Hospital, Loughlinstown, Prof. Neil Duignan of the Coombe Hospital, Dr. T. Hanratty, formerly of St. James's Hospital, Dr. George Henry of the Rotunda Hospital, Dr. Dermot MacDonald and Dr. John Stronge of the National Maternity Hospital and Ms. Ann Scott of Mount Carmel Hospital for all their help with information over the years. In this context I would like to thank Dr. Brennan, Prof. Duignan, Dr. Hanratty, Dr. Henry and Ms Scott for showing me round their units. A very personal "thank you" is due to Dr. Brennan for all her care and attention to me.

I would also like to take this opportunity of thanking Eveleen Coyle and Fergal Tobin of Gill & Macmillan who gave me so much encouragement, and Deirdre McQuillan for bringing us together!

Last but certainly not least, my loving thanks go to Bernard, Alexis, Catherine, Conor and Frances who put up with so much muddle and little attention while I was busy at the personal computer!

The quotations on pp. 31-2 from the Home Birth Centre newsletter, April 1983 are reprinted by kind permission of the Home Birth Centre.

All other quotations are from *Report of Survey on Experiences in Various Irish Maternity Units 1979-1980* and *A Report on Women's Experiences of Maternity Services (1985),* both published by the Association for Improvements in the Maternity Services, by whose kind permission they are reprinted.

The author does not necessarily agree with the views expressed in the quotations.

SECTION ONE

First Decisions

1

Becoming Pregnant

Finding out you're pregnant

The majority of women will suspect that they are pregnant when a period is missed. There are other signs of pregnancy, though not all women will experience all of them and some will not experience any at all. These include increased tenderness and an enlarging of the breasts, nausea, vomiting, increased urination, a change in taste, and constipation, all in varying degrees according to the individual concerned.

Most women want to establish that they are indeed pregnant as early as possible, and though this can be done by a doctor carrying out an internal examination, the pregnancy is usually confirmed by means of a test on the woman's urine. Only a small amount of urine is required for these tests, which are usually performed about two weeks after the last period should have begun, though newer tests claim to detect pregnancy even earlier.

There are a number of places where you can get a pregnancy test done. Your GP may be able to do it for you, or he may send the sample to the nearest hospital for testing there. Some maternity hospitals will do pregnancy tests on an outpatient basis, though you would have to check with your nearest unit about this. If you live near to a family planning clinic, they will have the facilities there for doing the test. In Dublin the LIFE organisation also offers a testing service. Lastly, many chemists now stock do-it-yourself pregnancy testing kits, containing all the necessary equipment and chemicals. The manufacturers claim that if the instructions are followed carefully, the tests are as accurate as any other, and they do offer an alternative for women who don't have ready access to other places. Some kits now include two tests so that if the first result is negative or unclear, you can repeat the test later.

Single mothers

If you find yourself as a single mother-to-be, there are a number of voluntary agencies that you can contact for help and advice. All of them will treat your situation in complete confidence, so don't hesitate to contact them — their services are free.

Ally offers the single mother the opportunity of living with a friendly family during the final stages of pregnancy, and provides a counselling service on all aspects of single parenthood. Ally also introduces mothers to other relevant agencies and services that might be of use and interest to them.

Amie aims to provide the necessary services for single pregnant mothers and one-parent families within Co. Mayo.

Barnardo's provides a counselling and support service for single parents, and gives practical help with ante-natal and post-natal problems. Barnardo's will also give assistance with finding accommodation, day care facilities and liaison with adoption agencies.

Challenge works in the Kilkenny area providing counselling and support services including pregnancy testing, the provision of ante-natal accommodation, social welfare, limited foster care, help with adoption, day care and continued support for those keeping their babies.

Cherish is a non-denominational organisation providing a service for single women during and after pregnancy, with the emphasis on self help and mutual support. It offers the following services: information and advice to personal

4

callers and by letter and phone; counselling; specialised advice on social welfare allowances, taxation, legal aspects, medical matters, day care, retraining and employment opportunities; practical help such as second-hand cots, prams and baby clothes; limited short-term accommodation; group meetings every month for single and expectant mothers.

CURA was established by the Catholic bishops to provide a confidential referral, information and counselling service for single mothers throughout the country. Contact is usually made by phone, though person-to-person meetings can be arranged.

Federation of Services for Unmarried Parents and their Children (FSUPC) is a national, non- denominational body which promotes the welfare of single parents and their children. It provides an information and referral service during and after pregnancy, and it aims to co-ordinate all services and research in the area of single parenthood. The FSUPC publishes a very informative *Directory of Services in Ireland for Unmarried Parents and their Children.*

LIFE (Ireland) is an organisation which actively opposes abortion and started its services to provide practical help for women with "problem" pregnancies. LIFE offers a telephone service for help and advice; an office-based counselling service; free pregnancy testing; help with accommodation; pre-natal and post-natal support service.

Open Line Counselling provides pregnancy testing facilities, and gives non-directive counselling and post-pregnancy support.

Protestant Adoption Society and Single Parent Counselling Service is, as the name suggests, concerned with two kinds of service. They emphasise that the single parent counselling is run quite independently, and that by consulting them you are in no way committing yourself to placing your baby for adoption or even considering it.

Despite its name the service is completely inter-denominational and offers single parents counselling and information during and after the pregnancy. The services include the arrangement of medical care; accommodation either with a family or in a mother-and-baby home; financial advice; help with seeking employment and accommodation after the baby is born; and, if such a decision is reached and required by the mother, advice on placing the child for adoption.

There may be other services provided in your own locality by different agencies, such as social service councils — the National Social Service Board can provide you with this information. Similarly the FSUPC's *Directory* lists a number of agencies in different parts of the country.

Useful contacts: addresses of above in Appendix 3.

Infertility
You may be surprised to find a section on infertility in a book about pregnancy, birth and children, but it is a fact of life that a certain percentage of women do have difficulty in conceiving (sometimes after having borne one or more children), and therefore some brief remarks on the subject have been included here. Do note, however, that if you feel you have a problem you must take medical advice — only the very basic outline of the subject is included here — so do go and discuss it with your GP. Don't be shy or, even worse, feel ashamed — the doctors are there to help you, and the sooner you go, the sooner investigations, advice and treatment (if necessary) can be started.

All of which begs the question — how long should you wait before you consult the doctor? The usual advice is that you should have been trying to conceive for at least a year, but this is only a rough guideline — it will depend on your age (there will be more urgency where an older couple is concerned), general and specific health problems. Probably the best overall advice is that if you begin to think there's any problem, go and see your doctor. No one will be cross if you get pregnant in the meantime!

It always used to be assumed that the problem of infertility lay with the woman, but modern research has shown that this is not so. In about a quarter of cases the problem lies entirely with the man, and in about half of cases there are factors affecting both partners.

It is usually the woman who initiates the consultations about infertility, and the doctor will take a detailed medical history, probably including some questions about the male partner. At this stage he may also make an examination of the woman, partly to check on her general health and partly to see if he can spot any obvious problems. In a very small minority of cases it is found that intercourse has never fully taken place, and of course if this is the reason, then advice and encouragement can easily be given.

If nothing obvious is found at this time the doctor will probably indicate that he wishes to start further investigations, but it would be as well, if he does not suggest it, to suggest yourself that your partner is examined. The tests and treatment for female infertility become progressively more complicated as time goes on, whereas it is comparatively simple to test male fertility. The doctor will enquire about any illnesses or diseases that may have affected sperm production and he will also tactfully enquire if there are any problems with erection or the ejaculation of the seminal fluid. In conjunction with this, the man will be asked to produce a specimen of semen — for some reason, many men seem embarrassed when asked to do this, although women have to submit to all sorts of tests and examinations without a murmur! However, the purpose of producing this specimen is to examine the quality of the semen, and it can be produced in several ways — either by

7

ejaculating into a clean jar or directly from the woman's vagina a few hours after intercourse. The doctor will tell the man which method is preferred. The semen is then examined in the laboratory, and the test can of course be repeated if necessary. If the man is found to produce semen which contains no sperm, then he is completely infertile and unfortunately nothing can be done about it at present. If, however, the problem is one of low sperm count, for example, where not enough sperm are present in the seminal fluid to allow conception, then the doctor can advise on the necessary action to take.

It is only after this investigation has been completed that further tests should begin on the woman. You will probably be consulting a specialist in the subject at this stage, but the first investigation will find out if and when you are ovulating, or producing an egg. This is usually done by recording your early morning temperature, using a special thermometer which shows the slight rise that occurs at ovulation. Your doctor will tell you exactly how to record the necessary information and for how long. Drugs are available if there appears to be a problem connected with ovulation but must, of course, be taken under close supervision. Multiple pregnancies have occurred with these drugs, but the dosages are much more exact nowadays and you should not spend too much time worrying that you will produce quads or quins! The next step would be to check that the Fallopian tubes are not blocked, as if they are, then the egg and the sperm cannot reach each other. This test is usually carried out by using special equipment to blow carbon dioxide gas into the uterus and seeing whether it passes through the tubes or not. This test can be repeated if necessary. If and when a block is found, further tests can show where the blockage occurs so that surgery can be carried out, if appropriate.

These are only the most widely used procedures; if you

require further investigation then of course your specialist will advise you. A word must be mentioned here about artificial insemination and what have popularly become known as "test-tube babies". The legal position of donor insemination — that is, insemination of the woman with semen from a man other than her husband — has not yet been clarified here, but it is offered by the Dublin Well Woman Centre. If the male partner is proven infertile, then you may wish to consider this option, and you should consult the Centre for further advice and counselling.

The whole question of "test-tube babies" or in-vitro fertilisation, to give it its proper name, is an exceedingly complex one, and it is not proposed to go into the pros and cons here. Suffice to say that a technique has been developed whereby eggs can be extracted from a woman and fertilised with sperm outside her body and then returned in the hope of a pregnancy occurring. This is being done here in Ireland but there are fairly strict guidelines about the whole procedure and you would receive much advice and counselling before this option would be considered.

Useful contacts: Dublin Well Woman Centre
Any family planning clinic
National Association for the Childless.

2

Choosing a Hospital

Unfortunately for many women in this country, this chapter isn't going to be much use to them unless they are prepared to travel to one of the larger centres of population. Outside Dublin and Cork most women don't have a choice as far as maternity hospitals are concerned. They have to attend the nearest one because it's the only one in their area — though "nearest" is a bit misleading here. Some women have to travel thirty miles or more each way for each ante-natal visit and when they're in labour. Many small units have been closed down as being uneconomic to run as well as for other reasons given below, and though it is undoubtedly costly to have maternity units catering for a small number of births per year, women will often recall how enjoyable the stay in such a place was — the staff were friendly and unhurried, you were the centre of attention and interest, and the hospital routine could be quite flexible to suit your own particular needs.

Unfortunately the maternity section of this wonderful maternity hospital is being closed down and all mothers will have to travel a journey, for some, of forty or fifty miles.

One advantage of giving birth in a smaller hospital is that there is only one bed in the labour ward, so one doesn't have to listen to other people's problems — one can just get on with coping with one's own!

It is now the policy of the Department of Health that all women should have their maternity care in and have access to units staffed by consultant obstetricians and paediatricians, and that the minimum number of deliveries per year in each unit should be approximately 1500 to 2000, allowing for the sparsely populated nature of some areas. It is also argued that only these larger maternity units can afford the new technological apparatus that has come to play such a large part in modern obstetrics, and indeed we are fortunate to have such technology available when the need arises. However, for the large number of women who have normal, healthy trouble-free pregnancies these big hospitals can often mean an impersonal atmosphere, hurried staff, long periods of waiting to see doctors and rushed examinations with no time to ask questions or discuss worries.

One answer might have been to make increased use of the smaller units for those women with perfectly normal pregnancies and only refer those with problems or potential problems to the larger hospitals. It is argued that we cannot afford to take these chances, that it is difficult to predict which mothers will be at risk and that all mothers and babies deserve the best possible care, which they do — but many women might feel that a long journey, often by public transport, followed by an hour's wait in a crowded room for a three-minute examination by a different doctor at each visit is not what they would regard as good care. Don't despair entirely — there are alternatives, such as combined care and out-clinics (see chapter 4 for further details) which can save you time and travelling, so do enquire about them.

In some areas such as Dublin and Cork there is a choice of hospitals. In the Dublin area there are three maternity hospitals: the Coombe, the National Maternity (usually referred to as Holles Street which is where it stands) and

11

the Rotunda. There are two general hospitals with maternity units: St. James's and St. Columcille's in Loughlinstown, south Co. Dublin, one private hospital with a maternity unit (Mount Carmel) and a nursing home catering for maternity patients (Stella Maris). In Cork there's a choice between Erinville Hospital, St. Finbarr's, the Victoria and the private hospital, Bon Secours.

In theory, of course, there is nothing to stop you attending any hospital that you want to go to, and a number of women who are able to travel do decide not to go to their nearest unit but make a conscious decision to give birth elsewhere. However, this is only feasible if you are willing to travel not only for at least part of your ante-natal care but also in labour and to be some distance away from family and friends.

I didn't go back to the first hospital because the nursing staff were horrible to me over breastfeeding. I only went to this one because they allow demand feeding.

It is the most convenient hospital — comparatively speaking — for where I live, and the consultant has clinics in our nearest town which saves a lot of travel.

If I was pregnant again I would return to the same hospital as I feel they have the facilities to cope with an emergency, and are generally considerate and caring for the mothers and babies.

Public and private patients
What are the differences between going privately and publicly for your ante-natal care and afterwards? As a public patient you will receive exactly the same medical scrutiny that you would as a private patient. Your ante-natal care is free, and you will not have to pay anything for your

hospital stay as long as your income is below a certain level (see chapter 5 for greater detail on this). The minus points are that you will probably spend a lot of time waiting around at the ante-natal clinic, with perhaps not much privacy during the various tests and examinations, and in many hospitals, especially the bigger ones, you'll see a different doctor at each visit.

As a private patient you should see the same doctor each time (allowing for holidays, when you may have to see a colleague or locum), and in hospital you'll be in a private room if one is available. Note that the hospital cannot guarantee to put you in a room on your own when the time comes, and you may have to spend a day or two in a semi-private or public ward until one becomes available. At the moment all hospitals reserve the right to use single rooms for special cases whether the mother is a private patient or not. You stand a better chance of getting a private room in some hospitals than in others.

Women attending as semi-private patients will be booked in to semi-private accommodation i.e. they will share with up to five other women (though you may only have one other person in some units) — a kind of compromise between the single private room and the larger wards.

Private hospitals and nursing homes
It is as well to distinguish between these two types of units. In the past there was perhaps not all that much to choose between them but now they are two very different things.

Private hospitals often have nicer buildings than ordinary hospitals and the fittings and decorations will be more lavish than otherwise — for example, many private rooms will have a bathroom *en suite*. There is a lot more privacy, obviously, because nearly everyone is in a single room, though there are usually semi-private rooms as well, and the staff will quite often be less hurried and have more time to attend to you. Visiting rules are often more relaxed, so that it can be easier for your family to visit you, and usually there will be no problem in having other children in to see you.

On the minus side you should be aware that such places can be more expensive than being in a private room in other units, because you will pay not only for accommodation but also for delivery charges, drugs, medical sundries and nursery fees, for example. If you are covered by VHI, though, all of this can be recouped apart from nursery fees and one or two minor things such as newspapers and phone calls (see chapter 5 as well).

You may find that some people will try to put you off going to a private hospital with tales of the lack of medical cover. Certainly this has been true in the past, especially in relation to paediatric emergencies, but over the years the private hospitals have raised their standards and would be able to cope with all but the most extreme problems. However, if you have any doubts about this, check with your GP or with the hospital itself.

There are now very few nursing homes that cater for maternity patients and though they may offer the comforts of a hotel you must be aware that they are not equipped to cope with obstetric or paediatric emergencies, usually having little more than basic nursing care available. Very, very few women actually have their babies in a nursing home; they are mostly used by women who give birth in one of the bigger hospitals and then transfer within 48 hours of delivery to more restful surroundings before they return home.

List of maternity units

Maternity units have been listed under the Health Board area in which they are situated. It should not be taken as an exhaustive list — some of the smaller units in the process of being closed down have been omitted but may still be admitting patients, while others may close in the future. You should also note that a few units are planned or are actually under construction at the time of writing, and these have been included under the appropriate region. If in doubt you should check with your GP, your Health Board or with the hospital itself.

Eastern Health Board

Coombe Hospital, Dolphin's Barn, Dublin 8. Tel. 537561 (537775 for clinic appointments)

Mount Carmel Private Hospital, Braemor Park, Churchtown, Dublin 14. Tel. 961211

National Maternity Hospital, Holles Street, Dublin 2. Tel. 608788

Rotunda Hospital, Parnell Street, Dublin 1. Tel. 748111 (786921 for clinic appointments)

St. Columcille's Hospital, Loughlinstown, Co. Dublin. Tel. 825800

St. James's Hospital, James's Street, Dublin 8. Tel. 537941

Stella Maris Nursing Home, 17 Earlsfort Terrace, Dublin 2. Tel. 761340

The following units are planned:

James Connolly Memorial Hospital, Blanchardstown, Co. Dublin.

County Hospital, Naas, Co. Kildare.

Tallaght Hospital, Tallaght, Co. Dublin.

Midland Health Board

County Hospital, Mullingar, Co. Westmeath. Tel. (044) 80221

County Hospital, Portlaoise, Co. Laois. Tel. (0502) 21364

County Hospital, Tullamore, Co. Offaly. Tel. (0506) 21501

Mid Western Health Board
Cahercella Hospital, Ennis, Co. Clare.
County Hospital, Ennis, Co. Clare. Tel. (065) 21208
Regional Maternity Hospital, Ennis Road, Limerick. Tel.
  (061) 55455
County Hospital, Nenagh, Co. Tipperary. Tel. (067) 31491

North Eastern Health Board
County Hospital, Dublin Road, Dundalk, Co. Louth. Tel.
  (042) 34701
County Hospital, Monaghan. Tel. (047) 81811
Our Lady of Lourdes Hospital, Drogheda, Co. Louth. Tel.
  (041) 7601
St. Joseph's Hospital, Lisdarn, Co. Cavan. Tel. (049) 31399
A new unit is proposed at Our Lady's Hospital, Navan, Co.
  Meath.

North Western Health Board
District Hospital, Donegal Town. Tel. Donegal 19
General Hospital, Letterkenny, Co. Donegal. Tel. (074)
  22024
Sligo General Hospital, The Mall, Sligo. Tel. (071) 2161

South Eastern Health Board
Ardkeen Hospital, Waterford. Tel. (051) 73321
Carlow Maternity Hospital, Carlow. Tel. (0503) 31106
St. John's Maternity Hospital, Aut Even, Kilkenny. Tel.
  (056) 21172
St. Luke's Hospital, Freshford Road, Kilkenny. Tel. (056)
  21133
Waterford Maternity Hospital, Airmount, Waterford. Tel.
  (051) 75966
County Hospital, Wexford. Tel. (053) 22233

Southern Health Board

County Hospital, Bantry, Co. Cork. Tel. Bantry 133

Bon Secours Hospital, College Road, Cork. Tel. (021) 42841

Erinville Hospital, Western Road, Cork. Tel. (021) 21991

St. Finbarr's Hospital, Douglas Road, Cork. Tel. (021) 966555

County Hospital, Tralee, Co. Kerry. Tel. (066) 21222

Victoria Hospital, Infirmary Road, Cork. Tel. (021) 966211

Western Health Board

General Hospital, Castlebar, Co. Mayo. Tel. (094) 21733

Regional Hospital, Newcastle Road, Galway. Tel. (091) 64141

Portiuncula Hospital, Ballinasloe, Co. Galway. Tel. (0905) 2140

3

Doctors

I felt his attention to me was good and he was responsive to my questions.

The doctor was very aloof. He never offered information, but he answered any questions I had. It would have been very unsatisfactory if I wasn't well read on the subject.

I felt sure that if I needed to discuss any problems with her she would listen patiently.

Since private patients can choose which doctor they will attend and public patients, for the most part, have no choice in the matter, some of this chapter will not be applicable to all readers. However, even if you are attending publicly you may still like to check with the following sections to see how the professionals you come into contact with match up.

I was satisfied with him as a medical technician but not as a human being.

He gave me full attention and discussed all my problems with me.

I had confidence in him, but one was a number rather than a human being.

What should you be looking for in a doctor? Medical skill can be taken for granted, although if you have any special problems such as repeated miscarriages or diabetes, for example, you may be referred to a certain doctor who specialises in the management of them. Apart from this there are a few questions you should bear in mind. Is reasonable time allowed for each appointment? This can vary enormously, with some doctors booking women in at ten minute intervals (or even less), while others may allow twenty minutes or half-an-hour for each appointment. Has he got a relaxed, unhurried manner — you should feel that he's really taking an interest in you as an individual. Does he tell you what's happening — what the various tests and checks are for, what your blood pressure is and so on. Is he willing to discuss any worries with you? Does he encourage you to ask him questions? Is he willing to discuss any ideas you may have about the birth? In other words, is the doctor willing to treat you as an intelligent, healthy, individual mother rather than as a faceless case to be processed through routinely at each visit?

I felt rushed — I felt I was being pushed through in a rather mechanical way, although any questions I had were always answered, if somewhat shortly. The doctor's show of being uninterested (and bored) did finally reassure me that I must have a very routine pregnancy.

The doctor always seems in a hurry and just waiting to usher in the next patient.

With my previous babies ante-natal visits were a source of tension and friction. This time I had a woman doctor and she was actually a source of reassurance and friendship during the whole pregnancy.

Private patients

Even attending privately you may not have much choice of doctors if you live outside the bigger centres of population. A number of the smaller units will only have one or two consultants, in which case there's not much you can do unless you're prepared to travel very much further afield. Assuming, though, that you do have a choice, how can you go about finding the right doctor? There are several possibilities, but remember that none of them are infallible — personalities are notoriously difficult things to match, and what suits the woman next door won't necessarily suit you, so keep your own character and attitudes in mind. You may want to find a doctor who will treat you as an equal and who will discuss all the options with you, while other women may prefer a doctor who will make all the decisions for them, while others are somewhere in between.

You can ask around among your family and friends who've had babies recently. If you've already decided which hospital you want to attend, you can ring up and ask for a list of the doctors' names. You can look in the Golden Pages under the heading "Doctors" and find those with MRCOG or FRCOG (Member or Fellow of the Royal College of Obstetricians and Gynaecologists) after their names, though not all their names are included. Your GP should be able to suggest some names. Or you can ring one of the voluntary groups working in the childbirth area — both AIMS (Association for Improvements in the Maternity Services) and the ICT (Irish Childbirth Trust) can give you information.

You should note that there's no absolute guarantee of your doctor being there at the delivery (though most will do their best to attend). Even consultants take holidays and get caught in traffic jams! What you are opting for by attending privately is seeing the same person throughout your pregnancy and having privacy during your hospital stay. Just because your doctor does not actually deliver the baby is not sufficient reason for refusing to pay his bill!

Public patients

You may wonder who all the doctors are that you see at the clinic or hospital. The hierarchy of hospital doctors is like this: consultant, senior registrar, registrar, senior house officer and junior house officer, though not all hospitals have senior registrars or distinguish publicly between the house officers. In the three Dublin maternity hospitals there is also a "Master". He (no women so far!) holds office for a period of seven years and his job is a mixture of policy maker, administrator and public relations officer, in addition to his normal medical duties.

Public patients usually see a different doctor at each ante-natal visit, and this can be anyone from the Master to a newly qualified houseman, or even a student still in training. In theory you should be informed if a student is to examine you, though this is not always done, and you can object if you feel very strongly about it.

At some hospitals, however, it is policy for public patients to see the same doctor each time, as far as possible, while in others mothers are assigned to a "team". This, for example, might consist of a consultant, a senior registrar, a registrar and three house officers. In theory this gives "continuity of care", but in practice many women complain that they are lucky to see the same doctor twice in the course of their pregnancy. Because you may well be seeing a different doctor each time, it is vital that any special problems or requests are noted on your record card (see the section on ante-natal clinics) as this will be the only permanent link between each examination. There is a problem here in that on one hand all women should be entitled to continuity of care whether they attend as private or public patients, and yet on the other hand the junior doctors have to get their experience somewhere — and "somewhere" is usually in the public clinics.

It is in this regard that the smaller units may have a sort of advantage because, if they have only one or two consultants and perhaps two or three senior registrars, then it is far more likely that you will see the same doctor each time, or at least get to know the two or three who take the ante-natal clinics.

It was very unsatisfactory — always a different doctor or student.

As it was, the name on my card meant nothing to me. I saw him twice, and a different doctor every other time.

On my two previous pregnancies I attended privately and I found that as a public patient I received more attention and was given more time with the doctor.

4

Other Options

There are some other options which may be open to you regarding ante-natal care and delivery. These are what is known as "combined care", a midwives clinic, a planned early discharge from hospital after the birth, and a home delivery.

Combined care scheme

Combined care simply means that your ante-natal care is shared between your GP and the maternity hospital where you are booked to have your baby. What usually happens is that you ask your GP if he is willing to look after you during your pregnancy, or alternatively he suggests this option to you. If this option is chosen, you will make an initial visit to the hospital for what is called the booking clinic — in other words, so that the hospital will book you in for delivery. This first visit to the hospital ante-natal clinic is just like anyone else's, but for the next six months or so you will see your own GP instead of attending at the hospital. Then at approximately 34 weeks of pregnancy you will return to the ante-natal clinic, which will have received a record of your ante-natal care from your GP, and you will attend the hospital for the last six weeks or so.

This scheme has its critics. Some GPs feel that the hospitals don't really trust them as far as ante-natal care is concerned, and that too many women are recalled to hospital clinics after the booking visit for unnecessary reasons; on the other hand obstetricians argue that they cannot afford to take the slightest risk with the health of either mother or baby and that they must ensure that everything is progressing well. Many mothers, though, have said how preferable combined care is to attending hospital clinics: they already know their GP and he knows them, they see the same person each time, and they have a definite appointment time to see him. For rural women it can mean the difference between spending an hour or less on a visit rather than taking up the whole day. The only trouble, from the mother's point of view, is that having built up the relationship, she has to return to the care of strangers for the last month of pregnancy and for the delivery itself. Not all GPs are willing to operate the combined care scheme — for one thing they are poorly paid for doing so, and at present are only paid for providing six ante-natal visits — but it may well be worth thinking about this option to save time and travelling for a few months at least. If anything abnormal or suspicious does show up during your visits to the GP he will, of course, immediately refer you back to the hospital for further examination.

I felt my own GP did just as much for me, in fact I would say more. At the hospital you were just another cog in a wheel to them.

I felt I got more attention, explanation and time from my GP, and although the waiting time wasn't as long as I'd expected, the time with the obstetrician wasn't worth the distance I'd had to travel.

Midwives clinic
This was started as an experiment in early 1984 at Holles Street, as it was felt that many women related better to

another woman during pregnancy, and has continued since then.

This option is offered to women who are attending as public patients and who are receiving all their care at the hospital — in other words, if you opt for combined care you cannot also choose to attend the midwives clinic. You should also note that your medical and obstetric records will be taken into account, and if you have any previous or existing conditions that would need special attention, you will have to attend the ordinary clinic. You should, however, check on this if you would like to attend the midwives clinic, as each case has to be considered separately.

A consultant is on hand to be called in if required for a second opinion and to see each woman approximately three times during her pregnancy, but otherwise the clinic is staffed entirely by midwives. Each woman is accompanied throughout her visit by a student midwife so that a two-way process goes on — the student is learning how the woman feels about her ante-natal care, while the mother can ask the midwife about anything that is puzzling or bothering her. The senior midwives who staff the clinic soon become familiar to the mothers, so that a much closer relationship can be built up.

St. James's Hospital is planning to start staffing some of its "out" clinics entirely with midwives as from January 1986. Perhaps this idea will spread to other units in the future.

Planned early discharge

Planned early discharge is more common in the UK than in this country because we lack the back-up of community midwives here. If, like a number of other women, you would prefer to have your baby in hospital but then to return home as soon as possible after the birth, it is worth discussing this idea with the doctor, but be prepared for

Coláiste Oideachais Mhuire Gan ...

opposition. Provided that the birth is normal and that both you and the baby are fine, home may then be the best place for you. Breastfeeding may be easier to establish when you are not constrained by hospital routine, and if you have older children you may be happier to be back with them — as long as there's someone else in the house actually caring for you and them! The hospital may be more willing to agree to this arrangement if your GP visits you at home during that first week after delivery (some GPs will agree to this, so it's worth asking about) or if you can find a midwife who will visit — you would have to pay for this service, of course.

The National Maternity Hospital now routinely offer a 24 or 48 hour discharge to all mothers having their second or subsequent baby, and this option is discussed at the ante-natal clinic towards the end of pregnancy. Most hospitals, though, say that both mother and baby should stay for observation and rest, though often this latter word is a bit of a joke, as anyone who's been in hospital before will tell you.

In any case, planned early discharge is something you should keep an open mind about. If it appeals to you — and for many women a week in hospital is like a holiday, despite all the routine and interruptions — ask about it during your ante-natal visits and make the necessary arrangements, but wait and see how you and the baby are after delivery. If you're both well, then keep to your plan, but if you're absolutely exhausted, or the baby needs to stay in a little longer, be flexible and stay in as long as necessary.

I kept worrying about the two other little ones, with just my young sister to look after them. My husband had the farm to do as well.

I felt if I were to go home, once it was all over, I would have been so happy.

I felt great, no problems with self or baby, and I wanted to get into my home routine and out of the hospital one.

I was in such rotten physical shape that I wanted to stay in longer than I'd planned.

I felt confident with the baby by the time I left. Earlier I think I'd have been nervous with her.

Home delivery

In recent times the trend has been for all women to have their babies in hospital. The reasoning behind this was that most obstetricians felt that hospital was the safest place for both mother and baby in case of complications or an emergency, and until recently the number of women having their babies at home had fallen to less than 1% of the total number of all births in Ireland.

Some women felt, though, that with the swing to complete hospitalisation, there had been a loss of what might be called the "human touch". Ante-natal clinics were sometimes described as being like cattle markets or conveyor belts, it was claimed that women became nothing more than names or numbers on their record cards, new technological advances could make the labour ward resemble an electronics factory, and hospital routines had no time or place for the needs and wishes of individual mothers and babies.

So, very gradually, there has been a small increase in the number of home births as some women have decided that hospital was not the best place for them and their babies. They wanted to know the midwife or doctor who would deliver the baby, they wanted their partners to be fully involved in the whole process, they wanted to be able to adopt whatever positions they wanted for labour and delivery and they needed to know that they would not be separated from their babies after the birth.

Sometimes parents seeking this option have encountered numerous difficulties along the way. To begin with, doctors and midwives prepared to do home deliveries have become something of a dying breed, as all the expertise has become centred in the maternity units. Now, however, there are signs that some GPs would like to see a return to at least some home confinements, and the Home Birth Centre keeps a list of both doctors and midwives who are prepared to assist with home deliveries.

I found a GP locally who would accept me and he put me in touch with the local health nurse who is a midwife. At our first meeting she refused outright but following subsequent letters from me to the Health Board she called to my house, explained the dangers and responsibilities involved and said I must have an obstetrician. This service I could not afford. She called to see me again and told me she would attend if I could arrange to have a doctor present. My doctor could not guarantee to be present. As my baby was due on Easter Sunday I didn't want to insist on having the midwife against her will, as I felt she was being honest with me. I get the impression that both she and the doctor were told by the Health Board to put me off.

Another problem is that there is no legal requirement in this country for health boards to provide obstetric flying squads — these were specially equipped ambulances with trained personnel who could be called out in cases of obstetric emergency (not just for home births). Those flying squads which were in operation have been disbanded, and the lack of this facility must be considered as a serious omission as far as home births are concerned.

My GP succeeded in fobbing me off by saying I must consider my baby's safety and that I'd be to blame if anything happened during the birth at home, when it could have been dealt with quickly and efficiently in a hospital.

You should make your decision about home delivery as early as possible in your pregnancy, because it may take some time to make all the necessary arrangements. Think about your reasons for wanting a home delivery, and be quite honest with yourself — don't do it just to be trendy, don't do it just because a friend is having one, or for any other superficial reasons. You must feel that this is the best possible option for you and your baby, and you must have the support of your partner in this. Weigh up all the pros and cons and make a rational decision. If and when you decide on a home birth, approach a group working in this area of childbirth for advice, and then start to make your arrangements.

No doctor was willing to attend me at home.

I didn't consider a home birth because the best medical opinion I could get indicated that for a first baby, at least, it seemed unsafe for both me and the child.

I couldn't find a doctor who was willing to assist me at home.

How to arrange your home birth
You are not legally compelled to have a doctor in attendance at the birth, but most midwives will want a doctor to be on call in case of an emergency.

In order to find a midwife and a doctor, you can visit your GP and ask him if he is prepared to do a home delivery. Be ready for him to say no, as few GPs do home deliveries now — and also be prepared for him to try and dissuade you. If he does refuse to attend you, ask him if he can refer you to someone else. If he doesn't know of a colleague practising home deliveries, or seems unwilling to give you such information, you can ask your Health Board for a list of obstetric doctors in the area. Alternatively and perhaps best of all, ask the Home Birth Centre if they know of any doctors near you, and if so, approach them directly.

Meanwhile you should also be looking for a midwife. If you have found a doctor by this time, then he may well be able to recommend one to you, or again try the Home Birth Centre. Unfortunately midwives willing to deliver a baby at home are in short supply, as student midwives in this country are trained with hospital practice in view, and probably very few will see a home birth. If you are really stuck and cannot find a midwife by other methods, you should write to the Area Nursing Officer at your Health Board offices. Inform her that you are expecting a baby (include the expected date of delivery), say that you want a home confinement and ask her to provide you with a midwife — this should all be phrased very politely, of course. Try to get these arrangements made as early as possible in the pregnancy, so that you don't spend the last six weeks worrying about where the baby is going to be born. In any case you *must* receive ante-natal care throughout your pregnancy, so ask your GP to provide this even if he won't do the delivery.

Assuming that you find a midwife and a doctor, the latter will usually provide your ante-natal care although the midwife may want to share this with him. In any case she will visit you at home occasionally. About three weeks

30

before your expected date of delivery the midwife will bring a sterile pack to your home containing all the necessary dressings, etc. She will discuss in advance what else you may need to provide, such as a receptacle for soiled dressings, disinfectant, etc., and she will probably want to see the room where you plan to have the baby.

If complications or certain conditions arise during your pregnancy, then your GP may refer you to hospital for further checks. If a genuine medical condition is diagnosed, then you must take the advice to have the baby in hospital. Similarly if there is a genuine emergency during labour and the midwife feels you ought to be in hospital, don't hesitate — go. Your baby is worth more than any principles of home versus hospital.

When you go into labour you should ring your midwife to let her know. Depending on how far advanced you are, she may come to stay with you or she may continue with her own routine and leave numbers where she can be contacted. She should return well in time for the delivery itself, and if an episiotomy (cut) is necessary she will call the doctor to do the stitching afterwards.

The midwife will continue to visit you for ten days after the baby is born. She may call twice daily for the first three days and then once a day after that. The doctor may also visit you but this is not necessary. The midwife will give the baby its PKU test during one of her calls (see chapter 15).

Your doctor will give you your postnatal check-up at the appropriate time and will also examine the baby when it is six weeks old.

I had a smashing home birth on Christmas Eve and had a lovely baby boy weighing about 9 lbs according to the kitchen scales! I was so delighted to have been at home where I was able to carry on fairly normally right to the very end. It was lovely not having to leave home, particularly on Christmas Eve.

A lovely experience — so glad it was all perfectly natural, no drugs and luckily no stitches or tears. We were really lucky with the midwife the Health Board provided — willing to listen and comply with our needs. She enjoyed the experience as much as us and said it was lovely to attend a natural birth and to see how lively the baby was.

Useful contacts: Home Birth Centre
                     Local health boards

5

How Much Will It Cost?

Everyone in this country is entitled to health care but some people have to pay for certain services. Basically you will fall into one of three categories, according to income: Category 1, Category 2 and Category 3.

Category 1 consists of people with what is called full eligibility. Because their income is below a certain level (which changes from time to time) they are entitled to the full range of health services, including those of a GP. They are entitled to medical cards, which should be applied for to the Medical Section of the local Health Board office. Medical card holders are entitled to maternity care service, in-patient treatment in a public ward and specialist treatment free of charge.

Category 2 consists of people with what is called limited eligibility. This applies to persons who do not qualify for medical cards and yet whose income is still below a given figure (also liable to change at short notice) or to persons who are voluntary contributors to social insurance. Such persons should apply for a Hospital Services Card to their local Health Board office. They are entitled to maternity care service, in-patient treatment in a public ward and specialist treatment free of charge.

Category 3 consists of persons whose income is above a given figure. They are not entitled to maternity care service. They are entitled without charge to hospital services in a public ward, but they must pay any specialist's fees. They

3

also have to pay any charges there may be for services such as ultrasound, pathology, etc.

Semi-private patients

The semi-private clinic is also known in some hospitals as the personal clinic and is a sort of halfway choice between attending publicly and the full expense of going privately. You may find that the choice of doctors is limited to the senior registrars — those doctors who have a great deal of experience and whose next position will be as a consultant — or it may include some of the consultants as well. For a smaller fee than you would pay as a private patient you attend this clinic and will normally see the same doctor each time; however, you will not be delivered by him unless he happens to be on duty at the time. You will also pay any extra charges such as pathology, ultrasound and so on. You will be accommodated in semi-private accommodation after delivery, which means that you will share with up to five other women. The charge for such accommodation is less than for a private bed.

Private patients

If you attend as a private patient, this means that you choose to attend a particular consultant and will visit him at his rooms, which will either be in the hospital or at his home (or occasionally in separate consulting rooms). The majority of women attending as private patients will also book private accommodation in the hospital i.e. a single room, but you may also choose to attend a consultant privately but book semi-private accommodation as above. In this case you will pay the consultant's fee as a private patient but only the semi-private accommodation charges. You will also have to pay for any pathology and ultrasound charges, and if you should require a section or other surgery, you will also have to pay the appropriate fees to the anaesthetist,

34

theatre charges, drugs and so on. In a private hospital you will probably have to pay a nursery fee as well.

It is not possible to give definite figures for any of these fees as they can change so quickly. You should ask about the consultant's fees when you are booking in with him, but at the time of writing (late 1985) you should certainly be thinking in terms of £350 and upwards in Dublin, and a little less elsewhere. Some consultants may allow you to pay something at each visit so that you're not faced with finding all the money at once at the end of your pregnancy — ask if this would be possible if it would be easier for you.

Hospital charges also vary. As from January 1986 a private room in a health board hospital will cost £88, £67 in county and voluntary non-teaching hospitals and £33 in a district hospital. The charges for semi-private accomodation will be £63.70 in a health board hospital, £50 in a county or voluntary non-teaching hospital and £25 in a district hospital. If you are going into a private hospital or a nursing home you will have to enquire about the cost. In some units you will have to pay a deposit when you are booking a bed, and this is deducted from the final charge, but check with your doctor about this.

VHI Insurance

The Voluntary Health Insurance Board provides cover for maternity patients as long as you have been a member for at least nine months by the date of delivery and provided that all your dependent children are members too. You can claim your hospital bill and consultant's fees from VHI as soon as they have been paid, but other charges such as ultrasound and pathology can only be claimed through the annual out-patient scheme at the end of your subscription year. Nursery fees and other miscellaneous items are not refundable by the VHI.

The cost of your hospital accommodation will be

refunded up to a maximum of five days following a normal delivery. The VHI issues a hospital directory showing which plan you need to cover semi-private and private accommodation in every hospital in the country, so you should check with this to see what your own insurance covers. A longer period can be claimed for where there are genuine medical reasons, such as a Caesarian section.

Your new baby should be added to your policy as soon as possible after birth. Then, if special neonatal care or treatment is necessary, this too can be claimed from the VHI.

It will depend on how many fee units you have in your VHI plan as to how much of your consultant's fee is repaid. However, if your fee units do not cover the full amount of the professional fee, you can keep the doctor's receipt when it is returned by VHI and claim up to a further £40 on it in your out-patient scheme at the end of the subscription year.

Useful contacts: VHI
                  local health boards

SECTION TWO

During Pregnancy

6

Ante-natal Care

Many women have passed through nearly nine months of ante-natal care and been left at the end wondering what it was all about, apart from the fact that they knew it was "done" to all pregnant women. Sometimes you might wonder why you are spending so much time sitting in queues with so little obvious result — until the final big day! — but if you understand why you are there, it can make the difference between a somewhat negative experience and a positive time of pregnancy. If you are aware of what is happening, you can help yourself to make it more positive by knowing what to expect — and by making sure that you are given the necessary advice and attention.

Ante-natal clinics

Private patients will be given a definite time to see their consultant, and often have a reasonably nice waiting room to sit in. In fact, a number of consultants do not see their private patients at the hospital but in their rooms — either in their private house or special consulting rooms — so check on this when you make your first appointment. You may occasionally have to wait for longer than would normally be expected, but in most cases you will find that this is due to the doctor having been called to a delivery. Don't grumble — it may be your baby he's called away to deliver one day!

39

Public patients, though, are often told to arrive at two o'clock, for example, only to find forty other women with the same appointment, and then it's a case of first come, first served. This can lead to very long waits, sometimes in rather unattractive surroundings, and is one aspect of the public clinics that receives much criticism from women. The best advice is to go prepared for a long wait — take your knitting, or a book or magazine, or some work, so that at least you have something to occupy yourself with. Or, if you're feeling tired, relax as best you can while you're waiting, rather than getting all tensed up about the inevitable delays. After you've been a couple of times, you may even note that you could come at a later time when most people have gone, so that you don't have to spend so long waiting to be seen. Holles Street in Dublin is currently introducing a proper appointment system for public patients.

Unventilated, overheated, uncomfortable and unsupportive seating, old magazines, no relevant educational material or details of support groups, etc.

No room for children. Crowded but just enough seats. Pleasant atmosphere — probably because of nursing staff attitudes.

Another cause for complaint in many clinics is privacy, or rather lack of it. If you are attending privately, you will see the consultant in his own room. You will be examined there, weighed, your urine sample will be tested and though your doctor may seem hurried, it's the rare one who actually turns you out before you're dressed again.

Women at the public clinics, on the other hand, are sometimes quite badly treated in this respect. You may be weighed in front of everyone, with those nearest being able to hear the result, and your urine may be tested in full view of all the other women. In some hospitals you will at least see the doctor in the privacy of a room, but in others there may be nothing between you and the woman on the next examination couch but a screen. In these conditions it can be very difficult to discuss anything with the doctor — you may be aware of the women on either side of you, and, when you're lying flat on your back, partly undressed, you can feel very much at a disadvantage and unable to carry on a proper conversation. You may also be aware of how many women are still waiting to see the doctor and so feel that you can't delay him any further with your queries — but do take the time, if necessary! You are perfectly entitled to ask a civil question and to get a civil answer, despite all the disadvantages of your position and surroundings.

Insufficient time to spot potential problems. No discussion with the patient. "Cattle market" atmosphere.

As a midwife who worked in the hospital I was really a VIP. I must say, though, that for the ordinary public patients there are long waits at the clinics and little consideration of their anxieties.

It never got less embarrassing each time I was there — a skimpy little curtain screening you off from the next woman, so you can hear everything said by the doctor, and you don't have to look very hard to see explicit shadows through the curtain.

Sufficient privacy, but an unnecessary amount of undressing to see the consultant, who merely listened to chest and felt tummy, for which we had to strip and wear a hospital gown.

To be fair, some hospitals are well aware of their shortcomings in the public clinics and are constantly trying to introduce positive changes, though many have old and unsuitable buildings to add to their problems. Overall, there are some points you should bear in mind, if you are to make any choices either about hospitals or clinics within a particular hospital. Look at the clinic times — are they all equally convenient for you? If you are still working either one first thing in the morning or one towards the end of the afternoon may be more suitable than one where you have to leave work and then return afterwards. If you are at home with children at school a morning clinic might be best so you don't have to worry about arranging for someone else to mind them. Is an appointment system used? Are clinics held in places other than the hospital itself? All the Dublin hospitals do this — staff travel out to clinics held in health centres or other suitable premises in areas such as Tallaght, Ballymun, Coolock, Dun Laoghaire, Ballyfermot, Wicklow and Arklow. Obviously this could save you a lot of travelling. Are there creche facilities for older children? The answer is probably no — this is a facility which would be much appreciated by many mothers but hardly any maternity units have one — space and staff are usually at such a premium that a creche is very low on the priority list. (In the long term this might be something that a group of local women — or perhaps younger unemployed people — could provide in co-operation with the hospital.) Are refreshments available for those attending the clinic? If you've had to travel a long way and/or have to wait around for a long time, you will probably appreciate such a facility.

Having decided which hospital you're going to attend (if you're lucky enough to have a choice), your first visit there will be to the booking clinic, if you're attending publicly. It is, by the way, advisable to start your ante-natal care as early as possible, and certainly by the sixteenth week of pregnancy. It has been found that there is a correlation between late attendance at ante-natal clinics and problems in babies, even stillbirths, so although the clinic might not be the most attractive place to spend part of your day, do go as early as you can in pregnancy. When you make your appointment for your first visit, ask if it is necessary to bring a GP's referral letter with you. Some hospitals insist on this and will not see you without one.

First visit

Your first visit, whether you attend publicly or privately, will be the longest, so don't think it'll take as much time each month. First of all a note will be made of all your personal details (and some regarding your partner) and then you'll be asked about your medical, surgical and obstetrical history. You may wonder why some of the questions are necessary: not only is the doctor building up an overall picture of you and your health, but also some of the details are used (anonymously, of course) to provide countrywide statistical information, such as the ages of mothers having babies, size of families, partners' occupations and so on. Try not to be embarrassed or upset if some of the questions seem too probing about your medical history or any other personal details — if there is anything relevant to the pregnancy in your life history that you would rather keep to yourself, don't worry about revealing it. The doctor will have heard similar details before from other women and won't be shocked, and in any case anything you say to him is told in confidence.

You'll be weighed and measured and your blood pressure will be taken. This provides what is called base line data for the rest of the pregnancy, as the doctor can see at a glance how much weight you've put on and if your blood pressure has gone up to a significant degree. A sample of your urine will be tested — this shows if there is any infection present. It is also tested to detect the presence of sugar and protein, which would alert the doctor to the possibility of certain problems. A blood sample will also be taken (or possibly two or three separate ones). From these samples the doctor can estimate your haemoglobin level (which tells him if you need iron or not) and he will also have the blood analysed for evidence of rubella (German measles) antibodies. One attack of rubella usually confers immunity for life, and this can be detected in the blood, but if the mother has no antibodies and contracts rubella in early pregnancy, there is a high chance that her baby will be born mentally and/or physically handicapped. All schoolgirls are now being offered rubella vaccination in early adolescence, which should protect future generations, but at the moment it is still essential to carry out the test. If no antibodies are detected, you will probably be offered the vaccination once the baby is born, as you must not be vaccinated while pregnant. (If you do unfortunately contract rubella in pregnancy, contact your doctor immediately for advice.) The blood sample is also tested for evidence of venereal disease, which could damage the baby if left untreated. Lastly, the sample is used to establish your blood group and rhesus factor, which is dealt with in greater detail in chapter 15.

You will then be given a thorough physical examination and sometimes an internal examination is done as well, though doctors differ on the necessity for this. In some hospitals all women are sent for an ultrasonic scan during or shortly after the first visit, while in others only a certain percentage of women are scanned. Not all hospitals have scanners, so unless you are attending a hospital in a large urban area, you may not have a scan at all.

For a scan you lie on a table or couch and your bare tummy is liberally rubbed with a special oil. Then the scanner is passed up and down your tummy while sound waves bounce off your uterus to form the complete picture.

This picture shows up on a screen, though you will probably have to have it explained to you by the technician as the outlines can be quite confusing, especially in early pregnancy. Scans can be used to estimate the age of the foetus and thus the estimated date of delivery, and can also show up some abnormalities. The presence of twins or triplets can be confirmed, and towards the end of the pregnancy the presentation of the baby can be shown — this means that the doctor can see which way the baby is lying in the uterus, such as head first or bottom first.

If you are sent for a scan, ask the doctor why it is being done. Some women object to a scan being done as part of the ante-natal routine, and certainly no one can insist that you have one, while others feel the pregnancy becoming real for the first time when they see the outline of the baby on the screen. The Royal College of Obstetricians and Gynaecologists has stated that ultrasound scans should not be carried out routinely, so if there is no obvious medical reason and you object to the procedure, say so.

Record card
The answers and results of all these questions and tests will be written on your record card. If you have any special requests or problems, make sure that a note is being made on your record card. As you may see a number of different doctors during your ante-natal visits, it is vitally important that accurate records are kept. A sample record card is illustrated in Figure 1. Some of the most common abbreviations that you might see are as follows:

LMP   (date of) last menstrual period
EDD   expected date of delivery
BP   blood pressure
           (always expressed as two figures e.g. 100/75)

Figure 1

The hospital record card

NAME MARY RYAN
ADDRESS 4 THE LANE
DUBLIN
PHONE
GP SMITH
8 THE ROAD, DUBLIN

D.O.B. 7.4.62
Age 23
Parity 1
LMP 4.11.85
EDD 11.8.86
Blood group O+

Date	Weight	BP	Hb	Urine	Other
4.1.86	126	110/80		NAD	4 WEEKS
1.2.86	126	105/70	11	NAD	"
1.3.86	128	110/75		NAD	IRON
29.3.86	130	110/80		NAD	FMF 4 WEEKS
26.4.86	132	110/85		NAD	" "
		Husband wishes to be at birth			

hb	haemoglobin (level of red blood cells in blood sample)	
Fe	iron tablets prescribed	
NAD	no abnormal deposit (in the urine)	
FHNH	foetal heart not heard (at the beginning of pregnancy)	
FHH	foetal heart heard	
FMF	foetal movement felt	
LOA	left occipito anterior	refer to
ROA	right occipito anterior	position
LOP	left occipito posterior	of the
ROP	right occipito posterior	baby's head
Vx	vertex (baby's head points downwards)	
Eng	engaged (baby's head has moved down into the pelvic brim ready for birth)	
T	term (40 weeks pregnant)	

These are only examples, as is the record card illustrated here. Your doctor or hospital may use another kind, but the basic information on it will be the same. If there's anything at all that you don't understand on your card, ask! You're perfectly entitled to an explanation, and in any case most doctors have come to realise that it's far better for a mother to understand what is happening to her rather than have her worrying from one visit to the next and possibly building up secret fears. Sometimes, just because nurses and doctors are so used to working in a medical environment they forget that something very simple to them can be quite puzzling or even frightening to a non-medical person, so do ask them to explain anything that isn't quite clear to you.

The staff were civil but did not volunteer much information. In fact they appeared surprised sometimes at being addressed by a patient.

They were always ready to listen and reassure. They always asked if there were any problems.

It was fair enough but one felt a bit rushed. However, if I had questions I always made sure to ask them and to get answers!

I felt confident that if anything went wrong it would have been spotted, but I got no information on any aspect of childbirth, and questions were not encouraged very much.

Special problems during pregnancy

Depending on the hospital you're attending, if any special problems crop up — diabetes, for example — you may be referred to a consultant within the hospital who specialises in its treatment, or your own doctor may continue to look after you. If you are attending a small unit you may be referred to a larger unit where more specialised guidance and treatment is available, but your own doctor should discuss this thoroughly with you.

I had a complication in the pregnancy and I was very nervous. My doctor saw me every two weeks at my request and in between if I needed to be reassured.

Other help

Sometimes there may be other problems weighing on your mind. You may be a single mother, or you may be living in overcrowded conditions, or trying to cope with a whole host of worries. If so, a medical social worker should be available to talk with you and advise you about your particular problem. Usually there is a notice at the ante-natal clinic to tell you where and when to find her; if not, ask one of the nurses or doctors. Don't feel shy about seeing her, because very often she can help you directly, or at least put you in touch with someone who can.

Attendance at the clinic

Unless you are seeing your GP for combined care, you will normally attend the clinic once every month until you are about seven months pregnant, then fortnightly for the next two or three visits and then weekly after that until the baby is born. The doctor will tell you if there is any alteration to this pattern and why.

At these visits you will be weighed, your blood pressure will be taken, your urine will be tested and the doctor will examine your tummy to see how the baby is growing. If you have any questions to ask at your visits, write them down — otherwise many women forget what they meant to say until after their visit is over!

Should anything unusual arise between visits, you can, of course, ring either the hospital or the obstetrician for advice, or your GP. Do not hesitate to contact them if you are worried about something, and if it is a real emergency, such as unexpected bleeding, do not worry even it if happens to be the middle of the night. There is always someone on duty at the hospital who will tell you what to do.

Looking after yourself

Ante-natal care, of course, is not just something that takes place once a month at the hospital or in the doctor's surgery, though we tend to forget there is more to it than this narrow definition! Ante-natal care also includes taking care of yourself, and thus your baby, by paying as much attention as possible to your own lifestyle. Within this definition we can consider nutrition, smoking, alcohol, care of the teeth and exercise.

Nutrition

Your doctor may have mentioned this subject to you, but perhaps not in any great detail, though it is now recognised that nutrition is very important for both mother and baby, even before conception, and it is certainly of prime importance during pregnancy and lactation. So you should discuss your diet, and also the need for any iron, multivitamin and folic acid tablets. Until recently it had become accepted practice to give these supplements to all women, but the tendency now is to move away from this blanket coverage and to selecting those women whose diets are really in need of supplementation. If the doctor isn't too forthcoming on the subject, there are several books you can read (see appendix 1).

In general, though, you should be eating as healthy and as balanced a diet as you can. This does not mean that you have to buy the most expensive foods but rather to balance your diet correctly. In simple terms you can divide your foodstuffs into four basic categories and then make sure that you eat something from each group every day. The four groups are:

1) **Cereals,** which are the foods to give you energy, and they include bread and other grain products. Within this food group be careful not to fill yourself up on white sliced bread and pre-sweetened cereals — brown bread made from whole wheat and with wholegrains is better for you, as are cereals in as natural a form as possible. These kinds of cereals also provide you with plenty of roughage which guards against constipation, a common complaint in pregnancy.

2) **Fruit and vegetables** will provide you with the essential vitamins and minerals. Try to buy and eat these foods as near to the raw state as possible — fresh rather than frozen, frozen rather than dried or processed, and avoid tinned fruits in heavy artificially sweetened syrups. Cook your vegetables for as short a time as possible to

preserve the minerals and vitamins. Fruit and vegetables are another good source of roughage.

3) **Meat, poultry, fish and eggs** are the protein foods. If you are a vegetarian who does not eat fish or dairy produce, you can get your protein from the various peas, beans and lentils (but if you are a vegan — one who takes no dairy produce at all — you should really take advice about your diet during pregnancy).

4) **Dairy foods** are rich in calcium, for building healthy bones and teeth, and include milk, cheese, butter and yoghurt. You can, of course, used skimmed milk, skimmed milk products and vegetable oils if you prefer. In fact, it is not absolutely necessary to drink milk at all — if, for example, you have an allergy you can take calcium tablets instead — but for most women it is a relatively cheap source of calcium and some protein.

Note that "junk" foods like cakes, sweets, biscuits and crisps are excluded from the above categories. This is because they have little, if any, nutritive value and should not form a regular part of your diet.

Care of the teeth
While on the subject of eating it may be as well to consider an essential accessory — the teeth! There used to be an old saying that went something like "A tooth for every child", meaning that it was usual for women who had had several children to have lost a number of teeth or to suffer from very bad tooth decay. This was partly due to poor overall living conditions, partly to poor diet and partly to lack of dental care. Nowadays, however, no woman should neglect her teeth during pregnancy (or at any other time, come to that) and she should certainly not give pregnancy as a reason for dental decay. If a good mixed diet is followed this will contribute calcium towards the baby's needs and if the refined sugars are excluded this will also help to keep the mother's teeth healthy.

51

Nevertheless, there may still be some problems that crop up during pregnancy, especially with the gums, and it is imperative that visits to the dentist should not be neglected at this time. Medical card holders are entitled to free dental treatment, and should enquire locally about the service. If you are an insured person you also qualify for dental benefit, and in the middle of 1985 pregnant women also became eligible for dental benefit on their husband's insurance. Your health board or dentist will give you full details of these schemes.

Smoking

We should all be aware by now of the danger to health of smoking, but during pregnancy there is another person to think about: the unborn baby. When you smoke, the nicotine from the tobacco passes through your bloodstream and the placenta and therefore affects your baby. The full extent of the damage that can occur to the foetus is not yet known, but it is known that smokers suffer more miscarriages and that babies of smokers are likely to be smaller, are more likely to be born prematurely and are twice as likely to die during the first week of life than the babies of non-smokers.

It is also known that it only takes five cigarettes a day to cause this damage, and that the more you smoke, the greater the damage. However, if you stop smoking before your pregnancy, your baby will develop normally, so don't worry if you smoked before you became pregnant. In fact, it's never too late to stop — as soon as you stop, your baby will benefit from a purer blood supply and any dangers will be lessened immediately.

Of course, it's very easy for someone else to tell you to stop smoking, but not always so easy to do so. Not much notice has been taken of the stresses that make people continue to smoke, and pregnancy can be a stressful situation in itself, apart from any other factors. However, you should try to stop, and if you cannot stop altogether, try to cut down as much as possible. The Health Education Bureau and Irish Heart Foundation jointly publish a useful little leaflet entitled *If you smoke, I smoke* which may help you, and the Bureau also publish an information pack designed to help you stop smoking. If your partner is a smoker, ask him if he would consider stopping as well, so that you can encourage each other, and if he's a non-smoker to begin with, he will, no doubt, be delighted to see you trying and give you lots of encouragement!

Drinking and pregnancy

In the past few years most of the public attention has been focused on the dangers of smoking and pregnancy, but more recently it has been realised that alcohol, too, can harm the developing foetus. Heavy drinkers may produce babies suffering from what is known at the fetal alcohol syndrome, that is, with low birth weight, failure to thrive after birth, facial abnormalities, heart problems and mental deficiencies.

While current research indicates that few babies in this country are born suffering from this syndrome, it also shows that a number of mothers are at risk of producing such babies. Since we do not yet know what is a "safe" level of drinking in pregnancy, it would be as well to limit alcoholic intake to the minimum. Many women find that they go off alcohol during pregnancy, especially during the first two or three months when the developing baby is most at risk.

Drugs

It would be as well to mention drugs here, apart from tobacco and alcohol mentioned above. We tend to think of drugs, especially these days, in terms of the more notorious ones — marijuana, cocaine, heroin and so on, and of course, addicts who become pregnant affect their babies by their habits, to the extent that babies can be born addicted to the particular drug and have to be detoxified in the first few days of life.

However, any drugs can affect the baby, even aspirin if taken in excess, and therefore it is wisest to avoid any medication if you can possibly help it, especially in the first three months of pregnancy when the various organs are developing. If you are buying any remedies over the counter, ask the pharmacist if it is safe to take the particular drug while pregnant; if you have to be prescribed any drugs by your GP during your pregnancy, remind him that you are pregnant as he can then consider the various alternatives and choose the safest. Fortunately doctors are much more aware now of the hazards to the foetus of drugs — you may not remember the thalidomide tragedy when mothers were prescribed a sedative which deformed their babies, but it did wake people up to the dangers of even properly prescribed remedies.

Of course, there are certain women who must stick to a regimen of drugs because their own health would be threatened without them. If at all possible it would be wise to discuss what will happen before you become pregnant — that is, will you need to take different drugs, a different dosage and so on. In any case, as soon as you become pregnant you must tell your doctor so that he can decide what to do about your drugs.

Exercise

As pregnancy is not an illness, you should continue to carry on as normal for as long as possible, although you will probably find that you tire more easily, especially right at the beginning and towards the end. Again, your doctor will advise you if you need to take any special precautions, but the majority of women can carry on with their favourite form of exercise for as long as they feel comfortable. (If you're attending aerobic exercise classes or something similar you might mention this to the doctor as some are not suitable for pregnant women.) Obviously your changing shape will mean that some activities come to a halt sooner than others, but a woman with good muscle tone is helping herself prepare for the hard work of labour. Apart from walking the best exercise is probably swimming, because it uses all your muscles and yet the water surrounds you so that you don't have to make too much effort — so if there is a swimming pool at hand, make the most of it!

Useful contacts: Foresight
                     Health Education Bureau

Work and Pregnancy

Maternity leave

Most women who work full time and some who work part time are eligible for maternity leave. As long as you fulfill certain conditions set out below you are legally protected by the Maternity (Protection of Employees) Act of 1981, which means that your job must be kept open for you to return to after your baby is born.

The basic conditions to qualify for maternity leave are that you must be working in insurable employment (that is, you pay contributions), you must work for at least eighteen hours a week and you must be returning to the same employer afterwards.

You are allowed fourteen weeks of maternity leave, of which four must be taken before the expected date of delivery and four taken afterwards. How you divide the rest of the leave is up to you. If you are feeling perfectly well during your pregnancy and are in a job that doesn't require a lot of physical effort, you may prefer to work as long as possible beforehand and take the remaining ten weeks afterwards. Alternatively, if it becomes apparent that you need rest while you are still pregnant, you could take more of your leave beforehand.

You should note that you are legally entitled to a further four weeks leave *without pay* in addition to the fourteen week period already mentioned, and you can take any annual leave owing to you. This extra leave can only be taken if you notify your employer in writing of your intention to do so at least four weeks before you would otherwise have been due to return to work. The maximum length of leave you are entitled to is twenty-two weeks.

You should tell your employer as soon as possible that you will be taking maternity leave, so that he can make arrangements to cover your job while you are away. You must give formal notice of of your intention to take maternity leave in writing, and the minimum notice is four weeks before you intend to start your leave — though presumably your employers will have spotted your state before this! Incidentally, you are not legally obliged to return to work after taking maternity leave, and if you do change your mind all you must do is give your employer the appropriate notice. For those who do return to work, you must give notice, in writing, to your employer at least four weeks before you intend to return, and this must be confirmed in writing between four and two weeks prior to your starting date.

Dismissal

You cannot be dismissed from your job just because you are pregnant. You are protected under Section 14 of the 1977 Unfair Dismissals Act, which states that the dismissal would be unfair if it occurred solely or mainly because of your pregnancy. Even if you cannot continue at your particular job within the company — because it would be potentially hazardous, for example — your employer should try to find you other suitable work. If you come up against any problems at work because of your employer's attitude towards your pregnancy, you should contact your union (if you belong to one) and/or the Employment Equality Agency at 36 Upper Mount Street, Dublin 2, who will give you detailed information and advice.

Ante-natal care

Under Section 16 of the Maternity (Protection of Employees) Act you are entitled to time off to attend for ante-natal visits and the postnatal checkup. There are no limits on how many visits you may make or on how long each visit may be, as this depends on individual circumstances. However, your employer is legally entitled to be informed in writing at least two weeks prior to each appointment, and he may also request you to show him your appointment card showing the time and date of the appointment, unless it will be your first visit. Some employers have been known to query the length of time spent at ante-natal clinics — many men find it quite extraordinary that visits can take so long. Do not be intimidated by this — you are entitled to be at the clinic, no matter how long it takes.

If you have not attended for your postnatal checkup during your maternity leave, you can take time off for this too, but the appointment must take place within fourteen weeks of the baby's birth. Again your employer is legally entitled to ask to see your appointment card.

Ante-natal classes

You are not entitled to take time off work to attend ante-natal preparation classes (although a few employers are known to permit and even encourage this). As most hospital classes are held during the day you will probably have to make alternative arrangements — see chapter 10 for further details.

Child care arrangements

If you have definitely decided to continue working after the baby is born, start thinking well in advance what arrangements you are going to make for someone to look after him. Some women have their mother or a sister who will do this, but most mothers will have to look elsewhere.

You may employ someone to come to your house to mind the baby and probably do some housework as well (an au pair might be suitable but she'd be living with you) or you may find someone willing to mind the baby in her own home. In both cases do check very carefully as to whether the person you choose is suitable. For example, is it more important to you that she cleans the house from top to bottom and leaves the baby to its own devices in the meantime, or would you prefer to return to unpolished tables and a contented, stimulated child? If you are leaving the baby at someone else's house, you may and should be able to find out a great deal about her before you come to a decision. Has she children of her own? If so, will they get unfairly preferential treatment? How will she amuse the baby as he grows up? Does she have suitable toys or will he be left to amuse himself — or worse still, plonked in front of the television? If she is to feed the child, and this is important as he grows older, what are her ideas about food? Will she give him good wholesome food or tend towards refined foods, crisps and sweets all the time? You may possibly have to come to a compromise in the end, but try to find someone who fits in with your ideas and standards as much as possible.

You may be one of the lucky few in this country whose workplace has a nursery attached to it — the universities are the only ones so far — or you may have to start looking round for a day nursery. These are relatively few and far between, but in any case you should check them carefully as some are much better than others in terms of facilities, attitudes, staff ratios, hours and so on. There are some nurseries run by the health boards and voluntary associations, but their places are usually reserved for the most needy cases. Lists of these nurseries can be obtained from your local Health Board, the Irish Society for the

Prevention of Cruelty to Children (ISPCC) or the National Social Service Board, and they are also listed in the FSUPC's *Directory*. However, it is more likely that you will have to turn to a privately run enterprise. These may be advertised locally or your local Health Centre may be able to give you information.

For a very useful book on the whole subject of child care you cannot do better than read Ronit Lentin & Geraldine Niland: *Who's minding the children?* (see Appendix 1)

Useful contacts: Local health boards
National Social Service Board
FSUPC
Irish Day Nurseries Association
Irish Pre-school Playgroups Association
ISPCC
St. Nicholas Montessori Society of Ireland

8

Maternity Benefits

Up till 1983 there were two main types of benefit that were payable to women during and after pregnancy: these were the maternity grant and the maternity allowances. The maternity grant was pitifully low, being only £8, but practically every woman could satisfy the conditions for its payment on either their own or their husband's insurance records. However, in the 1983 Budget the maternity grant was abolished and no payment is now made to those women who work in the home, apart from medical card holders who still receive the abysmal £8. In mid-1985 it was proposed by the Minister of State for Women's Affairs that a grant of £60 should be introduced under certain conditions but whether this will happen is not certain. (See Irish Women: Agenda for Practical Action (Stationery Office, 1985) Chapter 4, para. 4.15 (a), p. 115).

Women who have been or who are still working in paid employment may qualify for one of the two types of maternity allowance, depending on their insurance records and whether or not they are taking maternity leave from their jobs.

Maternity allowance: scheme for women in employment
This scheme applies only to those women who are taking maternity leave and returning to the same employer after the birth. You must satisfy the same conditions as for

maternity leave or you must have paid not less than 26 PRSI contributions in the twelve months immediately preceding the first day of your maternity leave.

This allowance entitles you to 70% of your earnings in the relevant tax year, and is payable for a period of fourteen weeks.

Claims forms are available from the Department of Social Welfare at Aras Mhic Dhiarmada, Store Street, Dublin 1 or from any local Social Welfare office. Your doctor must complete the "certificate of expected confinement" and your employer must complete the "certificate of maternity leave from employment" on the form, otherwise you will only get the general maternity allowance described below.

Maternity allowance: general scheme

Under the general scheme of maternity allowance, a woman who is not taking maternity leave but who satisfies certain insurance conditions may claim this allowance.

To qualify for this allowance you must have made at least 26 PRSI contributions at any time before the birth and have 26 contributions either paid or credited in the relevant contribution year. For 1986 the relevant contribution year will be the 1984/1985 tax year.

The allowance is payable for six weeks prior to delivery and for six weeks afterwards. If the birth occurs later than expected the allowance period may be extended. You should claim the allowance eight weeks before the expected date of delivery. Forms are available from the Department of Social Welfare (address as above) or any local Social Welfare office. Your doctor must complete the "certificate of expected confinement" on the form and you must make sure that your insurance number is entered correctly.

At the time of writing the general maternity allowance is £37.25 per week. You may also qualify for pay related benefit after four weeks (see below).

Pay related benefit

If you are claiming the general maternity allowance you may also qualify for pay related benefit. A separate claim is not necessary, as it will automatically be paid with your allowance, but you should have your P60 form (end of year earnings and tax statement) available as it may be required to verify your claim.

Pay related benefit is based on your earnings in the tax years before the benefit year in which your allowance started. (The tax year starts in April.) It is payable to women whose reckonable earnings (i.e. including overtime, bonuses, sick pay, etc.) are over £25 per week. Pay related benefit is not paid for the first four weeks of the maternity allowance period.

EEC employment and benefits

If your last employment was in another EEC country you may still claim the maternity allowance, and pay related benefit may also be payable. You should complete the forms as outlined above but return them to the Record EEC Section at Aras Mhic Dhiarmada, Store Street, Dublin 1.

Single mothers

If you are an insured person you are entitled to the above benefits as long as you satisfy the contribution conditions. However, if you keep the baby you will also be entitled to a weekly allowance provided you have never been married, remain unmarried and are not cohabiting. At the moment this is paid at the rate of £54.04 per week for a mother with one child, with £11.60 for each additional child up to five children and £9.95 for the sixth and subsequent children. This allowance is means tested and will be reduced if you have any other income. Claim forms are available from the Department of Social Welfare, Phibsboro Tower, Dublin 7.

Supplementary Welfare Allowance

If you have no income or are unable to provide for your dependents you may be entitled to supplementary welfare benefit. Under this scheme you may be eligible for supplementary benefit, fuel vouchers, children's footwear vouchers, free milk and exceptional needs payment. You should contact the Community Welfare Officer at your local health clinic or your local Health Board office.

Rates of payment

You should note that although some figures have been quoted here they are liable to change at short notice. For up-to-date information you are advised to contact the Department of Social Welfare who publish a number of leaflets on their services and the rates of payment at any given time.

9

Equipment for the Baby

Although this chapter is not strictly concerned with pregnancy or birth or the maternity services in general, its subject is nevertheless seen as being of absorbing interest, especially to the first-time mother, as apart from buying some maternity clothes for yourself, you will have to start thinking about gathering together some things for the baby. Some women do not like to get anything until the baby has actually arrived, but in purely practical terms it is much easier to do your shopping beforehand. It also means that you can spread the cost over several months.

This list has been pared down to the absolute minimum essentials, though in a couple of places alternatives are given so that you can choose what will suit you and your baby best. Of course, you, your friends and relations can add extra items as you wish, but the following will meet all the baby's needs for the first few months — it may seem a very small list, but would be perfectly adequate.

Clothes
— babygros in stretch material. These are available in a variety of sizes and colours and can be worn day and night, so you don't necessarily have to buy nightwear as well. The smaller sizes often have mittens as part of the cuff which makes them extremely suitable for winter babies.
— vests. These come in either envelope-neck or crossover tying style; there's no real advantage of one over the other

65

so it's a purely personal choice. You can also choose between wool and cotton — many mothers prefer wool next to the skin but some babies have an allergy to it, so watch out for this at the beginning. You should have at least four vests, but of course a few extra would be useful.

— jacket/coat/coverall — something to go over indoor clothes when you go out. In winter something like a coverall with hood, mittens and feet all-in-one is best, and saves the bother of hunting for bootees, mittens and a hat, one of which is always missing at the last minute! These coveralls are available in several fabrics such as quilted nylon or knitted materials. Otherwise you will need a jacket, hat, mittens and either socks or bootees. In spring or summer you may prefer something lighter and not so bulky, such as a pram suit or a jacket with a hood for windy days. Remember that a baby loses body heat very rapidly through the surface of the head, so do be careful especially with a very young baby.

— nappies. You will have to decide whether you are going to use terry nappies, disposables or a mixture of both.

The great advantage of disposables is that there is no steeping, washing and drying to be done, but on the other hand they are quite expensive. You will have to balance their cost with their convenience and against the cost (in time as well as money) of steeping, washing and drying terry nappies. A few years ago there were many complaints about the fit of disposable nappies — they tended to allow leakage, especially with smaller babies. New improvements are being made all the time and this does not seem to be such a problem now. Many brands now also have re-fastenable tapes so that you can check whether the baby needs a dry nappy without wasting the one being worn, if necessary.

There are also disposable nappy pads which usually fit into special plastic pants, although these do not seem so popular with the decreasing cost of the all-in-one disposable nappies. If you decide to use this type then you will need several pairs of the plastic pants, as they can become soiled along the leg edges.

If you decide to use terry nappies, or a mixture of terries and disposables, you should buy the best you can afford. Quality is important here because the nappies are going to be in constant use for two or three years, and you may be using them again with younger children. They also have to stand up to either boiling or chemical steeping, so they need to be both durable and yet soft to wear. Buy as many as you can — two dozen are better than one, and having some extras will save you worrying about getting the used ones washed and dried ready for tomorrow.

Shaped terry nappies are also available. They are made of two or three thicknesses of fabric and are roughly triangular in shape. They are certainly much neater to begin with, and a lot easier to put on if you're not used to folding nappies, but they become a bit skimpy for bigger babies. They also tend to wear less well because they are always pinned in exactly the same place and this can cause the material to fray, or even tear after a while.

If you are using terry nappies you will need plastic pants, which come in pull-on, tie-on and popper-fastening styles — the choice is yours. Plastic pants can be steeped in the sterilising liquid (see below) with the nappies but after a time they do tend to become rather hard and may crack, so keep an eye out for chafing on the baby's skin. You will need nappy pins to fasten them with — these are special safety pins with big guards at the ends, and you may prefer to use nappy liners as well. These are like paper tissues, only stronger, and used inside the ordinary nappy can prevent much of the soiling. They are easily flushed away.

You will also need at least one nappy pail — any bucket with a lid will do, but there are special ones with lips for pouring and fitted lids. Unless you boil the nappies each

time you should use a sterilising agent to steep them in —
several brands are available on the market, and you should
buy it in the biggest packs you can afford.

Sleeping and transport equipment

— crib/basket/carrycot. The baby will obviously need
somewhere to sleep, but this can vary from the very basic
to the wildest flights of romantic fancy. Some mothers like
to have the baby in bed with them at night, which is fine,
but you will still need somewhere to put him during the
day — the bed is not the best place because one day he will
surprise you by rolling off the edge. He would sleep quite
happily in a well-padded cardboard box or a drawer from
a chest, but most people will use either some form of crib
or basket, or a carrycot.

The crib or basket can be bought all ready lined and with
the mattress and matching bedding, but do remember that
while fairy-tale cribs all swathed in broderie anglaise look
beautiful, they can be highly impractical and the baby will
not be impressed in the slightest. In any case he will soon
grow out of it and to be quite honest, your money would
be better spent on other things. You can, of course, buy
a suitable basket in a shop and make a crib up for yourself.
Alternatively, you can use a carrycot (though it can be a
bit heavy and awkward to get up and down stairs by
yourself), and if it comes on wheels, then you don't
necessarily have to have a pram as well (see below).

— fullsize cot. Some mothers use this right from the start,
although a tiny baby looks very lost in it! You don't
actually need one until the baby outgrows his first sleeping
place.

— bedding. You will need sheets and blankets for both
the crib/basket/carrycot and for the cot. Old sheets can
be cut down to size and hemmed round to fit either. Instead
of blankets you may prefer to use a continental quilt or

duvet, as these come in both pram and cot sizes now. You do not need a pillow for at least a year, though once your baby is sitting up you can put one behind him for support when he's in his pram. NEVER put a pillow in a small baby's sleeping place, as he could easily suffocate in it.

— pram. These range from the very basic to the absolutely de-luxe, and it is really up to you to decide how much money you want to spend on this item. If you have a carrycot with wheels you don't have to have a pram as well, though this is a matter for personal preference. Think about the future — if you have another baby, you may wish to use the pram with a seat for the older child at the handle end, in which case you will need a fairly sturdy model. Also think about where you live and how you get in and out — if you are in a house with a front door then a big pram would be no problem, but if you live in a flat four storeys up and with no lift you might be better off with the carrycot and folding wheels. Think of storage too — where will the pram be when the baby isn't in it? Put away in a spare room or blocking the hallway and front door? Some mothers will put the baby to sleep in the pram all the time to begin with, and then you do not need a basket or crib as well.

Incidentally, if you are one of the mothers who does not like to buy the equipment beforehand, most shops will take a deposit and keep the pram for you. This is also useful if you're a bit stuck for storage space.

— safety harness. This is essential once the baby is beginning to move around, as if he is not firmly held in place he could easily wriggle himself over the side of the pram or upset its balance and tip over. In fact, you would be well advised to get two harnesses — the one from the pram can usually be used later in the buggy or pushchair, but you will also need one for the high chair.

— car straps. If you have a car then it is essential that

you should fit the appropriate straps to hold the carrycot in place. You can get models to fit saloons, hatchbacks or estates. We tend to be a bit careless about children and car safety in this country — for example, you will still occasionally see children perched on an adult's knee in the front seat, which is illegal for one thing and highly dangerous for another. In an accident the child would go straight through the windscreen, so always put children in the back and make sure they are restrained properly. Later on the carrycot straps must be replaced with a baby seat and then a special children's car safety harness.

A new idea just introduced into this country is a kind of padded reclining baby seat which fits onto the front passenger seat. It has been introduced from America, where apparently mothers prefer to be able to see their babies, and is intended only for very small ones. The baby is carried with his back to the windscreen and is, of course well surrounded by the structure of the seat. If you are interested in this device, enquire at your local car accessories shop.

— buggy/pushchair. There are many different styles ranging from the basic, easily collapsible buggies to very elaborate pushchairs. Again, as with the pram, you should consider how, when and where you are going to use it before you choose a particular model. Buggies are easy to fold and carry, but they don't give good protection from the wind and rain unless you buy the special attachments, which are sometimes a bit fiddly, and you can't hang lots of shopping bags on them without upsetting the balance. The heavier pushchairs can be awkward to fold down and bulky to carry, but they offer much better protection against the elements and you can often add a basket or tray for your shopping. So ask yourself which is the best for your lifestyle — do you travel mostly by car or by bus? Do you have to carry a lot of shopping? Do you have to walk to most places *and* carry a lot of shopping? Then decide which will be the best kind for you.

Incidentally, there are now models on the market which can be used right from birth, because the seat alters from being almost like a hammock to begin with, to being a conventional seat later on. Otherwise you're advised not to use a buggy or pushchair until the second half of the baby's first year, when he's able to sit up by himself. There are also models available in which the baby faces you rather than having his back to you, and yet others which can face either way.

— baby sling. This is not an absolute necessity, but its use is increasing in popularity all the time. Slings have become quite popular in the last few years, as you can carry the baby around with you and yet have both hands free to deal with other things. They are often very good for colicky or fretful babies who are comforted by the movement of the mother's body. They are also useful if you are going out on a shopping trip and don't want to be taking the pram in and out of shops and up and down stairs. There are several different models available on the market.

Other equipment

— toiletries. The two basic essentials are cream for the baby's bottom (vaseline does perfectly well for everyday use) and either baby shampoo or a bath foam which can be used for washing hair as well. You can buy special soap, if you wish, and most people like to have talcum powder to make the baby smell nice, though it's not essential. Neither is it essential to use one of the special cleansing lotions when changing the baby's nappy — plain water does the job just as well.

— flannel, towel and hair brush. You should have one of each specially for the baby's use, though as long as you wash your own towels regularly and thoroughly one of these will do. The hair brush should be a very soft one.

— cotton wool. You are going to use a lot of this, so buy the biggest packs you can afford. The bigger rolls are cheaper in the long run.

— baby bath. This is not absolutely essential, as you can use either the washbasin (but be careful of the taps) or a new washing up bowl of a suitable size, until the baby is big enough for the ordinary bath. You may be terrified at the thought of having to cope with this squirming soapy little creature while one hand is fully occupied trying to hold him properly: a new idea is a sponge mat that fits most baby baths so that the baby can be left lying safely in the water, cushioned by the foam, while you get on with washing him. Of course, this must only be used under close supervision — never leave a baby alone in his bath as it can take only a few seconds and a couple of inches of water to drown.

— changing mat. Again this is not absolutely essential, as you can always use an old towel, or a rubber sheer, or an ordinary nappy to put under the baby on either the bed or the floor.

— bottles and sterilising equipment. If you are going to bottle feed you will need the necessary feeding and cleaning accessories — see chapter 16 for more detail.

If you have already decided which formula you are going to use, you could buy a couple of packets to have ready in the house for when you come home.

— high chair. You will not, of course, need this until the baby is sitting up and beginning to feed himself, but you should be thinking about buying or borrowing one before you need it. There are a number of different models available, some of which will convert into small swings, or low chairs and tables, so have a good look at what there is.

These are just the very barest essentials, to which you can add as much or as little as you like. If you are in the fortunate position of being able to afford a very large item and you don't have one already, you might consider purchasing a washing machine or tumble dryer. They are expensive, of course, but they can save you endless time washing and/or drying clothes, especially if you are going to be using terry nappies.

Where to buy

Where are you going to get all this equipment and clothing? There are three main options — you can buy new, you can buy secondhand, and perhaps some items you could borrow.

— buying new. In the large urban areas you will have a choice of shops where you can buy all the items you want. There are specialist shops dealing solely with baby goods (look in your Golden Pages); some department stores will stock most if not all of what you need, and you should be able to buy all the clothing and bedding items from the various chain stores.

If you are in a rural area and don't have much choice, or perhaps are really too far from any suitable shops, you can buy by mail order. Ordinary mail-order catalogues may have a number of baby goods in their pages, although the choice will be necessarily limited. The very best kind of catalogue for baby goods is the Mothercare catalogue. It comes out twice a year, with a spring and summer edition and then an autumn and winter edition. It covers maternity clothes (including underwear), baby requirements and clothes for children up to ten. Goods can be delivered to any part of the country, and usually arrive within ten to fourteen days, although on larger items you may sometimes have to pay import duty. It is such a good catalogue that perhaps every mother ought to get a copy and look through it for ideas and to compare prices. A newer company which provides a similar service though with a slightly different range of goods, including the sponge mat mentioned above and lambskins for small babies to sleep on, is Babylove. See Appendix 2 for addresses.

— buying secondhand. You should not be ashamed if you cannot buy everything new for your baby — he certainly won't mind that his clothes don't come from the most exclusive boutique in the town! In fact, many mothers who could quite well afford new items will buy secondhand, especially baby clothes, as they are grown out of so quickly.

There are a number of sources for secondhand goods — jumble sales, bring and buy sales, mother and toddler groups (always a very good source), through small ads in the papers, noticeboards and in shops specialising in secondhand goods. The latter are opening at quite a rate, as more and more mothers realise that good quality clothes and equipment are in demand, especially in these fairly tough times.

The quality of clothes should be fairly obvious, but do be very careful when buying such equipment as cots and prams. You need to check that they are in good order: the paint on cots should be lead-free (though you can strip them down and repaint them yourself if necessary), and with prams or pushchairs you should check them very thoroughly, especially the brakes and folding mechanisms.

— borrowing. This can be useful for items that will only be used for a short time, such as the crib or the baby bath. Ask friends and neighbours with older children if they still have such items. They may also offer you extra clothes that would be useful to borrow.

If you are in very straitened circumstances, there are various agencies which might be able to help you. The Department of Social Welfare can give discretionary one-off grants for essential needs — see Chapter 8 for the details. Charitable organisations such as the St. Vincent de Paul Society may be able to help with clothing and equipment as well as money; you might wish to talk to your priest to put you in touch with the right person. Similarly some of the local Social Service Councils may be able to help you, especially with clothing. If you are a single mother, you should get in touch with Cherish, as they have a small supply of secondhand items of clothing and equipment such as prams and cots. (They will always welcome donations of such items, by the way, when you have finished with them.)

Useful contacts: Babylove
Mothercare
St. Vincent de Paul Society
National Social Service Board
Cherish

10

Ante-natal Classes

Many of the women I talked to had little or no understanding of what was happening to them. I think possibly the preparation and relaxation classes are not pushed enough by either GPs or hospitals, but I could be wrong and perhaps a lot of women are so terrified of the whole thing that they would prefer to know as little as possible. I know I could never have coped if I hadn't had a good stage-by-stage idea of what was happening to my body; at least I was never terrified because the preparation classes told me what to expect. I can only think it is fear that must be women's worst enemy in the experience of childbirth.

Many women now attend ante-natal classes, for a variety of reasons. If you wish to attend them, you will usually start when you are about seven months pregnant, but do enquire about them before this. If you want to attend classes at your hospital, you will usually see a notice telling you how to book for them: if not, ask one of the nurses at the ante-natal clinic.

Most women assume that in the classes they will be taught breathing techniques and relaxation exercises to help them during labour, but there's a lot more to the classes besides this, including the company of other pregnant women. You can compare notes without anyone getting fed up with the topic!

The physiology of labour should be explained to you — in other words, the class teacher will probably have what's known as a birth atlas, or a number of large diagrams showing a cutaway view of the pelvic region, and will be able to show you exactly what happens in each stage of labour. You should also discuss the care of the pelvic floor, as neglect of this part of your anatomy can lead to life-long problems.

You may also discuss methods of feeding: sometimes one class is devoted to the subject and perhaps a mother with a new baby attends to answer questions from class members. Some hospitals also offer mothercraft classes, on the care of a new baby, and you may like to attend these as well.

The classes were much more informative than my visits to the obstetrician, and any worries I had I discussed there.

They made you more aware of what was happening to your body, and I really looked forward to the class. It was the most relaxing time of the week.

The breathing and relaxation methods which are taught will vary from class to class and are based on a number of different ideas. You shouldn't worry, therefore, if a friend is attending different classes and appears to be learning totally different things — as long as the particular method suits you, then that's all that matters.

Though breathing and relaxation techniques can help many women, you should also be told about the different drugs that are available for pain relief during labour. It can't be emphasised too strongly that you are not a failure if you require such help in labour — labour is not an endurance test and no-one's going to think any the worse of you for taking pain relievers. On the other hand, be as well informed as you can be beforehand, as the different drugs have different effects on you and the baby. Chapter 13 deals in more detail with this topic.

The instructor talked down to the class. She gave us the impression that it was very much easier to have a baby than in fact it was. She instilled a false sense of confidence in natural childbirth. What was most useful was the knowledge I gained of hospital routine, choice of drugs offered and whether their offering was a medical or a social decision.

I feel that the approach and manner could have been warmer and less sterile and would like to see feelings and emotions discussed as well as physical things.

Preparation for your partner

Many ante-natal teachers now encourage partners to attend the course, or at least hold a special class for them. Often a film of birth is shown at this class. This is so that they will understand what is happening during labour and delivery and will not be disturbed by what they see.

A growing number of women want their partners to be with them during labour and at the birth, but don't feel a freak if either you don't want him there or he doesn't want to be there. That is your decision. The whole question of having your partner with you will probably be discussed at the class, anyway. Men still often have the idea that labour and birth will be all blood-and-guts and screaming women all over the place hanging onto the bed-head for dear life — a picture the media has sometimes presented up till quite recently — but nowadays this is just not so. Those who've actually been at a delivery will often say that though they felt a bit apprehensive and squeamish beforehand, once the labour started they became so involved that they forgot all about their previous fears. It can be very comforting for the woman to have someone she knows with her, and if for some reason your partner will not be available at the time, and you would like a personal companion, ask if someone else (friend, mother, sister — whoever you prefer) can accompany you. This may not always be permitted, but you should at least ask. On the other hand, of course, if you want to be on your own, again it's your decision and no-one else's.

The classes made everything very clear. My husband thought his preparation was excellent, and he was able to help very positively during the labour and birth.

Hospital classes

To return to the classes themselves, if you are attending these in hospital, you should be taken on a tour of the labour ward and delivery suite. This is very useful so that the place isn't completely strange to you when you're actually admitted. The teacher or the labour ward staff will show you around, tell you what all the various bits and pieces are for and probably let you try out the gas-and-air equipment which is available for pain relief. If there's anything you want to know about what will happen during labour and delivery, now is the time and place to ask about it. Incidentally, if you're attending classes elsewhere (or not attending at all) but would still like the chance to see around the labour/delivery suite, it should be possible to arrange this. Contact the Sister in charge to ask if this can be done — perhaps you could join one of the organised tours from the hospital classes, or it may be possible for you to arrange an alternative appointment for yourself.

In some hospitals classes are available for all mothers who wish to attend, while in others only those attending as public patients are catered for — due to constraints of both space and money. In other hospitals you may find that while all mothers are welcome, there will be one set of classes for first-time mothers, while others will attend different "refresher" classes.

In Dublin the Rotunda Hospital has now started taking its preparation classes to its mothers as well as the ante-natal clinics — it was recognised that some women might have difficulty in attending at the hospital itself, and so some health centres are now being used to give these classes. This is an excellent idea, and you should enquire if your own unit offers this service.

Contact with other girls who were pregnant — they were not all first-time mothers so questions were varied and more information forthcoming. Also, to meet some of the nurses from the hospital, and the exercises, were most important.

First-time mothers were given classes separate to others, we were discouraged from talking to previous mothers which made me feel something was being hidden from me. I would have liked time to have a chat together, maybe longer classes to give time for open discussion.

Alternative classes
Though most hospitals now offer ante-natal classes, you may not wish or be able to attend for a variety of reasons — the time may be inconvenient, especially if you have other children or are still working, and it may just be too far to go, especially if you live in a rural area. According to where you live you may be able to find some alternatives.

Many of the obstetric physiotherapists who run the hospital classes also offer private sessions, which may be at a more convenient time for you, and there are a few of these teachers who work solely in private practice. Some midwives also offer private classes. You could ask at the hospital to see if they can recommend anyone.

There should be classes in the evening for working mothers. I had to take time off work to attend them.

Only people who've already had children themselves should be allowed to give these classes. The hospital nurses had never given birth, so they said they didn't really know what a contraction was — and had no idea of the emotional aspects involved.

In Dublin the Well Woman Centre offers classes, conducted by a qualified midwife, and this course also includes classes after the baby is born, when you can practise postnatal exercises and discuss any practical problems encountered so far.

The Irish Childbirth Trust, which was originally started as the Irish branch of the National Childbirth Trust in England and is now an independent group in its own right, offers its own ante-natal preparation classes, also with a reunion held afterwards to discuss the experience. ICT classes are arranged to suit the mutual convenience of the teacher and the class, either during the day or in the evening, and all ICT teachers are women who've had children themselves. Individual teachers may also offer complete courses where both you and your partner can attend each class, if you so wish, but you should ask about this when you make initial enquiries. At present ICT teachers are based in Dublin (north, south and south-west), Co. Wicklow, Cork, Galway and Co. Clare, though as their network is expanding all the time you should enquire if any new areas are being covered.

There are also some teachers who specialise in various techniques and ideas, such as the use of yoga in pregnancy. You will probably hear about such people locally, though AIMS and the ICT may also be able to advise you on contacts as well.

Educating yourself

In many areas of the country it is a regrettable fact that no classes are available because of a shortage of trained personnel, and even when they are available, many women simply cannot travel the long distances to get to them. If you are unable to get to any classes at all, the ICT can supply you with leaflets dealing with different aspects of labour and delivery, so that you can do some preparation at home. You can write to them for a list of available leaflets.

There were no classes available in my part of the country, but I read as much as I could and practised the exercises at home.

There is a particular need in country hospitals for birth relaxation classes as I feel they would be of benefit to a lot of women.

I had to travel 27 miles to attend these classes — which were very useful — so I feel they should be made more widely available.

Classes were 40 miles away. I read everything in sight but in the long run could not prepare oneself completely.

Whether you are attending classes or not, you should read as much as you possibly can — about pregnancy, about labour and delivery, and about life with a baby. There are dozens of such books available, some good and some decidedly not so good, but you should be able to get hold of one or two at least. You will be more knowledgeable about what is happening to your body, which will help you — ignorance often leads to fear and tension, which in turn can create or worsen pain, but if you understand what's going on, you'll be more likely to relax and work with your body rather than struggling and fighting the sensations. See Appendix 1 for a choice of books on pregnancy, birth and child care.

Preparation for breastfeeding

If you are planning to breastfeed your baby you might also like to consider attending La Leche League meetings before the birth. The League was founded to give support and advice to breastfeeding mothers. LLL has an extensive network of groups in Ireland, and also publishes a number of leaflets on various aspects of breastfeeding which are available by post. Each group holds monthly meetings, which are open to non-members, and you would get some useful practical information by going along to these.

Leaflets on breastfeeding can also be obtained from the Irish Childbirth Trust. Further details about the services these two groups provide for breastfeeding mothers can be found in chapter 16.

Useful contacts: AIMS
Irish Childbirth Trust
La Leche League
Dublin Well Woman Centre

SECTION THREE

Labour and Delivery

11

Labour

During your ante-natal visits or at your ante-natal classes you should have been told when to go into hospital once your labour begins. You may also have been given a card bearing various details to bring with you, so that on admission your file and records can be located quickly. Towards the end of pregnancy check with the doctor what the particular hospital procedure is.

In many hospitals it is not necessary to ring them to tell them that you're on your way, but again, check about this. In any case, you won't be turned away simply because you didn't ring, so don't worry about it! If it has been agreed that you are to have an epidural, it will help the anaesthetist to be with you as soon as possible if the staff know you're on your way.

You should, of course, have arranged how you will get to hospital when the time comes, as you won't want to be looking round for a lift at the last minute. If your partner is driving you, ask him to keep the petrol tank topped up and make sure he already knows the way, while if you're planning to travel by taxi, keep the number handy (and the change for the phone, if you have to use a call-box). If for any reason you're really stuck for transport when labour begins, you can always ring for an ambulance. In some hospitals you will have been told the number to ring, as it may vary from district to district, otherwise look in the phone book or ask the operator.

What to bring with you

During your ante-natal visits you will probably have been given a list of things that you should bring with you when you are admitted. Items vary from hospital to hospital, but in general the following should be included:

— nightdresses
— slippers
— dressing gown
— personal toilet items (flannel, soap, toothbrush, toothpaste, etc.)
— two towels (one for you, one for the baby)
— size 3 sanitary pads
— sanitary belt or disposable pants
— nursing bras (if you are going to breastfeed)

As much as possible should be packed ready in advance — say two to three weeks before the baby is due — as you don't want to be hunting for everything at the last minute.

Due to the current economic climate you should note that some hospitals may ask you to bring in clothes for the baby to wear during your stay; you should check on this in advance. In any case you will need one set of baby clothes ready for the day you come home.

Admission procedure

Once you have arrived at the hospital a member of staff will deal with the administrative details. When you get to the labour ward you will be asked to change into your nightdress or a hospital gown (depending on hospital policy) and then you will be examined to establish that labour has indeed started and that everything is progressing normally. The length and strength of the contractions will be noted, as well as the intervals between them. Your pubic hair may be shaved, though the trend nowadays is to omit this. If you find that it is hospital practice to shave everyone, ask

88

if they would just do a perineal shave around the vaginal opening, rather than a full shave of the pubic area — the latter is horribly itchy when the hair is re-growing.

Similarly not all hospitals now give an enema to everyone. An enema empties the contents of the rectum, and can be done for a number of reasons: it can sometimes restart a labour that is slowing down; it allows more room for the baby's head to descend down the birth canal; to prevent mess and possible cross-infection when the baby is delivered, and also to save the mother from any possible embarrassment during labour if she involuntarily empties her bowels, as can happen. Certainly if the rectum is very full when labour begins you may prefer to have an enema to empty your bowels, so that you aren't worrying about an accident, but it isn't absolutely necessary. If you do pass any faecal matter at any stage during labour, the medical attendants will simply wipe it away — they've seen it all before and they definitely won't be cross or embarrassed.

Should you have an enema, either through choice or because it is hospital policy, the "pleasantest" method is to use disposable suppositories, which are like tablets and are placed in your rectum by the nurse; they will cause a bowel movement shortly afterwards. Some hospitals still use the soap-and-water method, in which a rubber tube is gently inserted into your rectum while you are lying on your side, and then soapy water is poured in via a funnel. This method can be uncomfortable and is rather messy, but try to relax as much as possible (use the techniques you've been taught) while the water is being poured in so that you don't tense up too much. Some hospitals have done away with enemas altogether, or only give them selectively. In any case, many women have the "runs" at the beginning of labour, almost as if the body were preparing itself, and if this has happened to you tell the staff and ask them if they would omit the enema.

In some hospitals you may then be allowed — or even encouraged — to have a bath or a shower, and this can freshen you up, especially if you've had an enema. A warm bath can be very relaxing during labour, but in some hospitals you will only be allowed into the bath if the waters have not yet broken. Other hospitals do not allow a bath or shower at this stage at all.

At some time during the admission procedures you will probably be asked to sign a form saying that you consent to any operative actions that may be necessary. This is to cover the hospital should an emergency arise, such as the need for a caesarean section or a blood transfusion — when every second counts, the staff don't want to be wasting time getting you or your next-of-kin to sign forms then. However, signing this form does not mean that procedures can be carried out against your will, and this can be especially relevant in the context of pain relievers. This is dealt with more fully in the chapter on pain relief, but you should be aware that you ought not to be given drugs if you have not asked for them, or if they have been offered and you have refused them.

In the labour ward
Once the admission procedures have been completed, you will be taken to your room or cubicle, and your partner should rejoin you if he has been excluded up to this time. (See Chapter 14 for some comments on this as well). In an ideal world each woman would be in a room on her own, so that she could walk around, lie down, listen to music or generally choose her own activities and positions for labour. In many hospitals, though, you will be sharing a room with at least one other woman and possibly more, and the most privacy you will get is curtains or screens around you. In some units you can walk around, which many women prefer to do in early labour, while in other units you are made to get into bed straightaway.

The nurse involved my husband very much in walking me up and down the corridor.

I found that walking about during labour helped me to cope tremendously.

We were encouraged to go anywhere we liked. We played Scrabble in the day room for the first three hours!

The nurses insisted that I remain on the bed, which I found most uncomfortable.

I stayed out of bed for the first four hours, watching television in the day room with my husband, and only took to my bed for the last hour or so.

Hospitals also differ on their policies regarding eating and drinking in early labour. It should be explained that once labour is established, the digestive process is temporarily halted and therefore food remains in the stomach. Should you feel sick, as women quite often do during labour, you may vomit, and though this does not matter in itself, there are other considerations. If you need a general anaesthetic at any time, there is a slight danger that vomiting can occur and that vomit may be inhaled into the lungs, where it can cause infection and even death. Nevertheless you are going to need a lot of energy for labour, and many hospitals will allow you to drink during labour. If you are not allowed to drink anything at all after you have been admitted and your mouth gets very dry, ask for some mouthwash to rinse it out, and it might be a good idea to have with you one of those special sticks for chapped lips in case your lips get dry as well. You may also be given small doses of magnesium trisilicate every two or three hours — this is a thick, chalky mixture, rather like Milk of Magnesia, and is given to lessen the likelihood of being sick.

Figure 2   Sample labour record

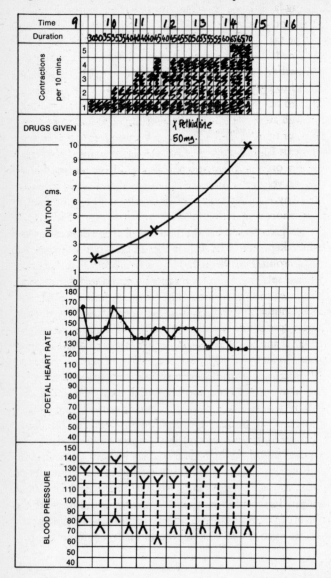

Monitoring

During labour you will be monitored constantly to check on the progress of labour. Your blood pressure and pulse will be taken at intervals and your temperature may also be noted. The length, strength and frequency of your contractions will also be noted — your partner is ideally placed to keep a record of these. The baby's heart will be listened to, and this is usually done by the nurse listening through a kind of miniature ear-trumpet which she places on your tummy. Tell her if a contraction is starting, so she can wait till it's over. Vaginal or rectal examinations are usually only performed when you are first admitted and then to verify that you are fully dilated and ready to push the baby out, but some hospitals have a policy of doing them more frequently, such as every two hours, to assess the progress of labour. A record of all these examinations will be kept on a chart similar to that illustrated in Figure 2.

Electronic monitoring has become one of the most hotly debated subjects in the context of labour. These monitoring machines can record the baby's heartbeat and the strength of the mother's contractions, and the results can be recorded on a paper printout. There are two kinds of monitor, an external and an internal one. With the external one a kind of belt is fixed around the mother's tummy (plus a second belt if the contractions are to be recorded as well), while with the internal one, fine wires with small electrodes are attached to the baby's scalp via the vagina. The internal kind can only be used once the bag of waters surrounding the baby has ruptured.

There is no doubt that such monitoring can be invaluable in cases of foetal distress, and should there be medical indications that this is so, you should have no hesitation in allowing this monitoring. It must be said, though, that a degree of over-use has and is being made with these monitors. Like a lot of the technological equipment now to be found in hospitals, these monitors are very expensive. They are purchased in all good faith to provide further information on a small minority of mothers and babies who need extremely accurate and continuous monitoring during labour, in case emergency action is needed, and it is marvellous that this can be done. However, once you have bought your expensive machinery you want to prove that it was worth all that money, or at least get your money's worth out of it, and so from using it on a very small minority who genuinely require it, you move on to use it on "borderline" cases, and then perhaps on to everyone, because you want to teach your students how to use it, or it just becomes part of the routine. This has happened here in some hospitals with the ultrasound scanner, for example, and at least one hospital in England has used electronic monitoring on all women in labour unless they object very, very strongly.

Like most things, there are two, if not more, sides to the argument. On one side women often find that they are uncomfortable when they are attached to a monitor as they cannot move round and change their position (though if an external monitor is being used you can ask a nurse or doctor to take it off temporarily while you get more comfortable). Some women also dislike the fact that with the internal monitor the wires are attached to the baby's head and feel that this must cause distress to the baby.

It has not been proved that in the majority of cases electronic monitoring is in any way superior to ordinary monitoring by a midwife. Also, machines can go wrong and give false readings or conversely, can be giving the right signals but be ignored by the staff who think it's a mechanical hiccup. Some obstetricians are very keen on using foetal monitors, saying that apart from the constant monitoring and the printed record of labour, the midwives are then freed from many routine tasks and have more time to spend with the mother in support. In this country many obstetricians are aware that some women have a genuine objection to being monitored electronically during a normal labour, and you should not be attached to a monitor against your will. If it is medically advisable that you or your baby should be monitored, then that is a different case altogether, and the reason should be explained to you. Of course, since this equipment is so very expensive, it is only the larger units that possess it, so you can check beforehand whether or not there are such monitors in the labour ward of your particular hospital.

It kept my mind occupied and I could compare the height of the contraction and knew when to adjust my breathing.

Sonicaid was used first — baby's heartbeat irregular. Nurse said she'd have to put me on the monitor. I asked if it would actually help the baby, and she said no, so I refused — there was no hassle, very co-operative.

The heartbeat was initially monitored using the trumpet which meant I had to lie down. This became increasingly difficult, so the midwives very kindly wheeled in a machine which could monitor while I remained sitting over the back of a chair — my chosen position. It made all the difference to the control I had over labour.

A newer form of monitoring is by telemetry, which allows a woman to move around during labour while the constant monitoring is in progress. This, though, is not yet in use in Ireland.

Companionship during labour

Many hospitals now allow a companion to be present during labour — indeed, some positively encourage it, though sadly there are a few units where the presence of a companion is an exception or simply not allowed at all. Fortunately these are now few and far between. Whether or not you have a companion there, the hospital may also have a policy of a one-to-one relationship between staff and mother during labour. In other words, as far as possible, one particular nurse is assigned to you for the duration of your labour and she will carry out all the necessary checks and report on your progress. Even if you do have a companion with you, this can still be very helpful — if you have any requests, you can ask "your" nurse — and even in the comparatively short time of labour you can build up a positive relationship between you. Of course, depending on the time of day and the duration of your labour, you may have two or even three nurses attending you as they change shifts and so on, but at least some effort is being made to incorporate continuity of care into the labour ward. Women who don't have anyone with them in labour often find the nurse to be a real companion and help to them.

I was left alone for long periods in the labour ward. The nurses were unwilling to admit my husband and it was the obstetrician who asked him in.

I don't think it can be emphasised enough the importance of having a familiar, caring face present throughout. I found the moral and physical support invaluable.

He was made to feel most welcome. I walked the floor all night and he slept in my bed.

My husband was not in the country at the time. I wanted a female friend to stay with me. They only allowed her to stay for half an hour. I would have liked someone present as I was very frightened.

My baby's father didn't support me during pregnancy, so a good friend stayed with me during labour and birth. I found her a tremendous support.

12

Induction and Caesarian Section

Sometimes the obstetrician will find it necessary to intervene in either pregnancy or labour. Those interventions which occur during the delivery itself are described in chapter 14, but induction and caesarian section are considered here.

Induction
Sometimes the obstetrician will find it necessary to perform an induction rather than letting a woman go into labour spontaneously. Induction simply means that labour is started artificially, and there are a number of medical reasons why it may be performed. For example, if the mother is suffering from a condition known as pre-eclamptic toxaemia (which is characterised by the presence of protein in the urine, high blood pressure and abnormal weight gain), or if she is a diabetic, or if the baby appears to be small for dates, then the mother may be induced.

In some hospitals there is an overall policy regarding induction so that, for example, all women who have gone fourteen days over their expected date of delivery will be brought in for induction, though the final decision will of course rest with the doctor in charge.

I was relieved to be brought in for induction as I'm not sure

I would have been relaxed as much while travelling to the hospital in labour.

Social induction

Induction for social reasons should be mentioned here. It means that labour is induced so that the baby is born on a particular day. It is possible that labour may be induced so that a baby about whom there is some concern is born when all the ancillary staff are still working — the various medical technicians, for example — but this is not induction for purely social reasons. No doctor here will induce your baby simply so that it is born on your birthday or your wedding anniversary or some other significant date.

Induction — for and against

If the doctor tells you that he has decided to induce you, ask him what the reason is for this. For a genuine medical reason, which should be fully explained to you, there should be no hesitation on your part. If, though, you are to be induced because of a general hospital policy, you may prefer to go into labour naturally, given that there are no medical indications to the contrary. Ask your doctor if he is prepared to wait for a few more days before performing the induction. If you have a longer than normal menstrual cycle — that is, longer than 28 days — then the expected date of delivery may be a few days out in any case.

The doctor wanted to induce me because of the breech presentation, but I was not agreeable to this before the due date, so he agreed to wait.

I still feel annoyed that I was induced before my time — it just so happened(!) that my consultant went on holiday the next day. It was a very violent start to labour as I went into

*immediate continuous contractions. I would only allow myself
to be induced again if I was absolutely sure there were good
medical grounds.*

Methods of induction

There are several different ways of performing an induction,
and the doctor may use one or a combination of these
methods.

One of the commonest and simplest ways of inducing
labour is to rupture the bag of waters surrounding the baby,
and is usually known as ARM, or artificial rupture of the
membranes. Normally the woman lies on her back either
with her legs spread apart or up in surgical stirrups (the
lithotomy position) and the doctor or midwife punctures
the membranes with an instrument that looks a bit like a
flattened crochet hook, or with special long blunt-nosed
surgical scissors. This allows the water (or amniotic fluid)
to drain away and labour usually begins shortly afterwards.

Rupture of the membranes is often combined with what
is commonly called "the drip". This, in fact, consists of
the continuous administration of a drug via a needle inserted
into a vein in your arm or the back of your hand to
stimulate the uterus to begin contractions. There are a
number of different drugs which can be used, but the most
usual one is oxytocin or syntocinon and, more recently,
the prostaglandins. Once the drip is in place a dextrose or
glucose solution may also be administered to prevent the
woman from becoming overtired during labour.

If the doctor decides to use this last method of induction,
you should be aware of two possible consequences. Firstly,
because you are physically attached to the equipment, you
will probably be unable to move around (though sometimes
a portable stand is used), and even in bed your movement
may be somewhat restricted because of the needle feeding
the drug into your vein. Secondly, many women find that

unlike most spontaneous labours, where the contractions build up in length and strength over a period of time, an induction may cause strong contractions almost from the outset. Sometimes it is harder to use your breathing patterns to cope with this kind of labour, because you feel you are starting in the middle rather than at the beginning. It may not necessarily happen like this, but you should be aware that it can.

The drugs for induction are sometimes administered as suppositories (like tablets) in the vagina. In this form they have an advantage in that you are not attached to a drip and can therefore move around if you wish. The drugs can also be given in tablet form to be placed in the cheek or under the tongue and sucked slowly, but the rate of absorption is not so effective and this method is rarely used, if at all, in Ireland.

Now I realise he induced me for a perfectly good reason, but he didn't tell me that and I felt very resentful and frightened. The drip made contractions extremely strong right from the start. I couldn't cope. I had lots of painkillers and the baby suffered from their effect.

Active management of labour

It might be as well to mention here what has become known as the "active management of labour". To some extent many labours are managed — or directed — by the obstetrician using induction, for example, or by breaking the waters and/or using a drip to speed up a labour that has slowed down. However, in recent years this active management of labour has become an accepted routine in some units and was, in fact, pioneered by Professor O'Driscoll at the National Maternity Hospital in Dublin. His method is based on the premise that women should be delivered within a given time, such as twelve hours. The policy of active management is applied to first-time mothers only who are carrying a single baby which is lying head down, so mothers with twins, breech babies, etc. are excluded. Before anything else is done, it is essential to confirm that labour has actually started, and the only evidence taken for this is the dilation of the cervix. Only when this has been confirmed will a decision be made to manage the labour. The woman may be examined internally more frequently than usual, and if after some time has passed she is not dilating at a certain rate — 1 cm. an hour, for example — her waters will be broken and she will be put on a drip, as described above, with the dosage regulated to speed up her labour.

This sounds terribly regimented and cut-and-dried, but there are some additional points to be made. Firstly, this regime is only employed when it is absolutely certain that labour is established, that is when good strong contractions and evidence of dilation are present. It is also flexible to some degree in that if a labour is seen to be progressing fairly well and dilation is occurring at a steady rate, intervention will not have been done just because a stated period of time has passed. Each mother is assessed by her own progress.

Obstetricians who employ this method say that it prevents both foetal and maternal distress, and that most women prefer to know that labour will be over within a certain length of time, and certainly Holles Street has consistently produced very low figures for caesarian sections. On the other hand many labours, especially first ones, may take a comparatively long time during the early stages, though the woman may be in no great discomfort and can cope quite well. If you feel that you would prefer to avoid such intervention, you should stay at home during the early stages and only go to hospital when your labour is really well established and you feel that you would prefer to be there.

Caesarian section

A Caesarian section may be performed electively (that is, the doctor has decided in advance that the baby will be born this way), or as an emergency once labour has begun. The reasons for performing a section are numerous: the health and interests of the mother and baby will be taken into consideration, and if you are scheduled for a section you may be confident that the safety of you and your baby is the doctor's prime reason. In any case the doctor should discuss the reason for performing an elective section, and even if you have to have an emergency section you should be given a quick explanation while preparations are being made. Above all, don't feel "cheated" if you have a section birth — some women feel afterwards that they have failed themselves by not giving birth normally, but while this is a normal reaction you shouldn't consider yourself a failure — the section will only have been done for very good reasons. If it is any consolation to you, Ireland stands out like a shining beacon in the statistics relating to caesarian sections — we have one of the lowest overall rates at about 6% of all births, with some hospitals having an even lower rate while in America the rate is somewhere between 15 and 20% of all births and still rising. Rest assured that this method was best for you and the baby and be thankful for modern operating techniques!

A section is performed exactly like any other operation in regard to the surgical preparation and technique. You will receive some pre-medication to dry up the secretions of the mouth and throat, but not the sedative that is usually given at this stage — you will be fully conscious when you go to the theatre. This is so that the baby receives as few drugs as possible. In theatre you may even be asked to

103

breathe in some pure oxygen via a mask — again, this is for the baby's benefit and not yours! Then a light general anaesthetic is administered — as light as can be so that the baby receives as little as possible. The actual incision into the abdomen can be made either vertically (in a line down from the navel) or transversely from side to side. With improved operating techniques it is now usual to make a transverse incision across the lower part of the abdomen — popularly called the "bikini cut" — which means that when the pubic hair regrows the scar will be barely visible. Occasionally, though, in an absolute emergency, the vertical incision must be employed as it is thereby easier and quicker for the doctor to get to the baby. Once the uterus is opened the baby is delivered, the cord is cut and the placenta removed. Usually the anaesthetic is deepened after the delivery while the incisions are being stitched up.

The baby will be examined by the paediatrician and may then be placed in an incubator. It may be possible for the baby to be taken out to your partner at this point, but not all hospitals will allow this, and in any case it will depend on the baby's state of health. In some hospitals it is policy that all babies delivered by section are kept in the nursery or even the special care unit for 24 hours at least, but if the baby is well and you are feeling reasonably ready to cope, ask if he can be brought to you. Doctors and nurses nowadays are much more aware of the need for mothers and babies to be together, and you should be reunited as soon as possible.

Epidural section

A new development in the past few years has been the epidural section. You can read more about epidurals in the next chapter, but here it will suffice to say it was found that since an epidural blocked all sensation in the lower half of the body, a section could be performed without a general anaesthetic being used. This has certain advantages for both mother and baby: the mother can actually see her baby as he is delivered, and the baby is less likely to need resuscitation because of the lighter anaesthetic effect.

Naturally there are many women who would be horrified at the thought of being conscious during the operation and who would much prefer not to know anything about what was happening. Others, though, feel that this is an excellent option when an ordinary birth is not possible, in that they see the baby within a few seconds of delivery, and can hold him almost as soon as they would with a vaginal birth; they feel that in some way at least they have participated in the event. Epidural sections are being performed in an increasing number of hospitals here, so if you know you will be having your baby by section and you think you might prefer this option, ask the doctor if it would be possible and discuss it with him.

Repeated sections

There used to be a saying which went "Once a section, always a section" and although this was true until fairly recently, modern operating techniques and improved surgical procedures make this less likely. There are numbers of women who have given birth by section and then delivered their next child normally.

However, it is not possible to give a general indication of who will and who will not have to have a section again. There are many factors: the reason for the original section, the health of the mother and baby in this particular pregnancy, general health and so on. Your doctor should discuss the probability of another section with you during your ante-natal care. It may be decided that another section will be performed, or he may decide to let you have what is called a trial of labour, in which you start labour either naturally or after induction, and a very close eye will be kept on your progress — in this case it is highly likely that electronic monitors will be employed if the unit has such equipment. Depending on your progress and the condition of the baby, you may proceed to a normal vaginal delivery or it may be decided after some time that another section will be necessary.

If you know you are going to have a section you might like to get in touch with the Cambridge Caesarian Support Society in England who produce a most useful booklet on all aspects of sections — it has been written jointly by doctors, midwives, and mothers so it covers many aspects. The handbook (see Appendix 1) costs about £2 sterling, including postage.

There is not yet a similar group in this country although it is hoped to set one up to give information, advice and support. If you have had a section already and would like to help, or if you are going to have one and need advice, or support after one, get in touch with the proposed Caesarian Support Group.

Useful contacts: Caesarian Support Group
Cambridge Caesarian Support Group

13

Pain Relief

There are a number of drugs which can be used to relieve pain during labour, but only the more well-known and often-used methods are considered here. Before these drugs are described, though, the breathing and relaxation techniques which many women learn at ante-natal classes must be mentioned.

Breathing and relaxation techniques

These are the techniques you will have been taught at your ante-natal classes, or you may have read about them and practised them at home. Not only can such techniques help you to work with your contractions, but also, because you know why you are using them you are less likely to become tense during labour. It has been known for many years that ignorance leads to fear, and fear leads to tension, but once you understand what is happening during labour, and why your body is working in this particular way, you are more likely to view labour constructively. If you have a companion with you — either your partner or a nurse — he or she can keep your rhythm going, especially during any bad patches when you might lose your concentration.

One marvellous advantage of using these techniques is that they have absolutely no side-effects on the baby, which is more than can be said for any drugs at all. It must also be said that many women use their breathing patterns almost as a form of distraction from the pain of the contractions — and there's absolutely nothing wrong with that!

As previously mentioned, of course, you should have no feelings of guilt or failure if you want or find you need some drugs to help with the pain. We are lucky that such help is available, and you should ask for pain relief if you simply cannot cope without it. One piece of advice: ask the nurse how much longer she estimates your labour will be. If she thinks you are getting towards the end of the first stage, you may decide that you will be able to cope without any drugs, or perhaps you could ask if you could use the gas-and-air (see below) but if you are still in the relatively early stages of labour, you should take the pain relief if necessary.

I wanted no drugs and the nurses never suggested that I needed them at any time.

Sedatives

Occasionally a very nervous or tense woman will need help very early in labour, before analgesia (or pain relief) is really required, and in this case a sedative or tranquilliser might be given to calm her. The most commonly used one in this country is valium, which causes the woman to relax, but it does, of course, pass through to the baby.

Analgesics

During labour these pain relieving drugs are usually given my injection. They can be taken by mouth but the absorption rate is very slow during labour and therefore the effect will be poorer.

The most common analgesic used in this country is pethidine, either on its own or in combination with another drug to prevent nausea. In this latter combination it is called pethilorfan. The recommended dosage is 50 mg to 100 mg every four hours, but this depends on the particular hospital's policy — in some units no mother may have more than one injection or receive more than 100 mg in total, and it may be as well to check on this when you are attending your classes or at the start of labour. Pethidine can be very effective in some women because it lets them relax or even doze between contractions, but other women complain that it makes them lose control of their labour pattern because it gives them a "woozy" feeling.

Pethidine definitely helped me to relax.

They were extremely helpful and helped me decide that all I needed was a half dose of pethidine when the contractions became very strong. I had had such a bad experience on my first when I had far too much and could not cope at all.

Pethidine proved completely useless — I was giddy and could not focus but the pain was just the same.

I became very disorientated and unable to control myself both physically and emotionally.

Just made me dopey but did nothing for the pain.

I dislike the feeling of falling in and out of consciousness.

Like all drugs, pethidine passes via the placenta to the baby, and if you receive large, frequent doses, or a dose towards the end of labour, your baby may well be born in a drowsy state, floppy to handle and uninterested in feeding. These effects can last for several days.

The ideal situation if you need an analgesic is to have a dose during the first two-thirds of labour, but once you are getting towards the second stage to see if you can manage without them. This, of course, is not always possible. For one thing, you only know how long the labour lasted after it's all over, but the nurse should be able to give you a rough estimate of how far you've got and how much longer you're likely to be. Secondly, if you have pethidine early in labour, you may not be able to cope with the much stronger contractions at the end of the first stage, and in this case perhaps using the gas-and-air apparatus might be helpful, rather than having another dose of pethidine.

Alternatively, you could ask if you could have a half-dose. This can take the worst edge off the pain without knocking you out altogether or making you lose control. This is sometimes a useful measure for women who experience what's called a "backache labour", where most of the force of the contractions is felt in the lower back rather than across your tummy. This often happens when the baby is lying in a less usual way, with its spine to your spine, or if its head is not completely tucked down onto its chest. The discomfort is practically impossible to control in these cases, since your breathing techniques can have little or no effect on it. The best form of pain relief is to be leaning forward, even on all fours if you like, to tip the weight of the baby away from your spine. If you cannot adopt these positions, a hot water bottle or an ice pack, or even clenched fists may help, but if they also prove useless, then a half-dose of pethidine can be quite effective in taking away the nagging edge of the back pain so that you can concentrate on handling your contractions.

Epidural anaesthesia
Epidural anaesthesia has become quite popular in recent years, but it is only available in certain hospitals, as it requires a very specialised technique to administer it. Smaller hospitals, therefore, may not offer this form of pain relief. Also, some hospitals will provide an epidural for any mother who wants one, while in other units it will only

be given if the doctor thinks it is medically necessary or advisable. For example, the condition of pre-eclampsia, very high blood pressure and uterine inertia (weak, ineffective contractions) may be considered as medical reasons in this context. Some doctors are also of the opinion that extremely young mothers should be given an epidural, though this depends on the particular doctor.

The epidural had an excellent result — enough was given at first and by the time I was ready to push it had worn off enough for me to move and feel sensation but no pain.

I found the epidural wonderful but as there is a lot of emphasis on natural childbirth, the mother who "gives in" can almost feel guilty at not having given birth naturally.

Basically the technique of epidural anaesthesia is the insertion of a needle into the epidural space in the spinal cord (your backbone) plus, if the anaesthetic is to be given continuously, a fine tube called a catheter. The anaesthetic is then injected via the needle and numbs the sensory fibres leading to the uterus. The injection can be topped up at intervals, if necessary.

In most women the epidural works perfectly well, but there can be some side-effects. Occasionally it doesn't "take" or only numbs part of the lower body so that the contractions can still be felt, and sometimes only one side of the lower body is numbed.

If the dosage is very precisely calculated and monitored, the effect can wear off in time for the woman to be in control of delivering the baby, but in many instances, because the nerves are still numbed, the mother cannot feel and respond to the pushing sensations of the second stage. In this case the staff will have to direct her when to push, and it is quite likely that the baby will have to be delivered with forceps, which means that an episiotomy will be done as well.

A few women have complained that after an epidural they were left with a bad headache or numbness in the legs. Tell your doctor if you experience these symptoms or if they persist.

One great advance brought about by the use of epidural anaesthesia has been the "epidural section", or a caesarean section performed with an epidural anaesthetic rather than a general anaesthetic. This is described in the previous chapter.

Inhalation anaesthesia

This is commonly known as "gas-and-air" or just gas. It is a mixture of nitrous oxide and oxygen, often called Entonox, and is administered from cylinders of the mixture via a mask. You can control this kind of anaesthesia yourself in that you can hold the mask and therefore breathe the mixture when necessary.

Gas is often offered at the end of the first stage of labour and during the second stage, when you are pushing the baby out. You should be shown how to use the apparatus if you are attending hospital classes, but if you need it during labour, the nurses will show you what to do.

I refused all pain relievers except gas and air which was a great help.

The first injection made me stiff and stupid and did nothing for the pain. Gas was much more helpful.

Local anaesthetics

A local anaesthetic is used for small surgical procedures and will be given to you if you require a forceps delivery, an episiotomy and/or stitching after the delivery. It is given by injection and takes effect very quickly.

General anaesthetic

A general anaesthetic will be given to you if a caesarean section is to be performed (unless it is an elective section and you are having an epidural). Also, if the placenta does not come away after the baby is born, or if parts of it are left behind in the uterus, you may have to go to theatre to have the contents removed. In this case a general anaesthetic will be necessary. Once this is administered you will be completely unconscious until after the operation.

TENS

A very new form of pain relief has recently been introduced and is called transcutaneous electrical nerve stimulation, or TENS for short.

The TENS systems consists of electrodes leading from a small battery-operated stimulator or central unit, which looks a bit like a transistor radio. The electrodes are attached to the skin with special tape or pads containing a gel to aid the conduction of the electrical impulses. The stimulator can be used in two ways: there is a low-intensity impulse which is given continuously, plus a higher-intensity stimulation which is controlled by the mother herself when she feels the need for extra pain relief.

As this method is still very new it is being studied in a number of trials. So far research seems to indicate that TENS is a useful aid to those suffering from low back pain during labour but is not all that good at helping ordinary contractions felt across the tummy. Also, it cannot be used to full advantage if the baby is being monitored electronically because of interference to the monitor. However, if you suffer from low backache or back pains in labour, TENS could be of use, and so far it appears to be free of any harmful effects to either mother or child.

Only a few hospitals here are using TENS, so probably the majority of women won't yet have an opportunity of trying it out. If it is available in your particular unit, the nurse or doctor will show you exactly how to use the controls on the stimulator.

14

Delivery

The staff were excellent and very accommodating to my husband and myself regarding his wish to be present and mine to have natural childbirth, not to cut the cord, etc.

It was not a really joyous occasion because the staff were too business-like and not sympathetic.

When you are nearly ready to deliver your baby, you may be removed from the room where you have spent your labour, or you may stay there, depending on the particular hospital. The standard delivery room is equipped with a high firm bed onto which you will be moved, and this may prove rather difficult if you're trying to cope with the urgent pushing sensations of your body. The bed is high, by the way, so that the doctors and midwives don't suffer from permanently bad backs after bending down to deliver babies; it can seem extremely high and narrow when you're up on it (but see below for some alternatives). There will also be a warmed cot for the baby, plus various other equipment that may be needed.

Can your partner be there?

You should already know what the hospital policy is on partners being present at the birth. An increasing number do admit partners to the delivery room but there are a few that refuse permission. This often has a lot to do with the attitudes of the staff working there rather than the buildings — some of the most progressive units in the country are housed in very old buildings, so "lack of space" and so on are very poor excuses.

It also used to be true that single mothers were discriminated against in this context, even if they were in a stable relationship, so that the father was refused admission for no other reason than the lack of marriage lines. Fortunately this appalling discrimination is decreasing. Indeed, some hospitals make a point of saying that if the father is unwilling to support the mother, then another companion of her choice may accompany her, and this is to be highly commended — for all mothers, not just single ones.

You should be aware, though, that no woman in labour has the legal right to have the companion of her choice with her. You can state your wishes positively but don't get angry or abusive. Someone had to be the first in every unit, and if yours is rather backwards in this aspect, perhaps you and your partner could break new ground. If your partner does want to be there and it's not hospital policy, keep asking, get it noted on your card during your ante-natal visits (if possible) and write to the consultant in charge saying that you are both very keen for him to be there. If enough people keep asking, things have to change eventually.

Fathers are actively encouraged to be present at the birth. This was the first occasion that my husband was present and I found it extremely helpful.

We were both pleased with his treatment. He was made very welcome and we both felt quite relaxed.

It was a shame he couldn't be at the delivery considering that the rules were changed within a few weeks.

Who will deliver the baby?

Until fairly near the birth you may not know exactly who is going to deliver your baby. If you are a private patient your own doctor will have been contacted, and though he will make every effort to get there, this is not always possible. There is always a doctor on duty in the labour ward, and he may deliver you. Alternatively, in some hospitals it is policy that midwives do most of the deliveries — after all, they are the experts of normal birth, and you can rest assured that they are extremely experienced and very, very capable.

Occasionally you may be asked if a student (either doctor or midwife) can perform the delivery. Naturally you may feel that you would rather have a more experienced person to deliver your baby, and you can, of course, refuse your permission, but on the other hand the students do have to learn their techniques somewhere. They are closely supervised by highly experienced personnel who will quickly take over if necessary, so really you should have no hesitation in allowing a student to take part.

Of course, there is a difference between one student being part of the intimate atmosphere of birth and having a whole roomful of people watching you. This, of course, might not bother you, but if it does, complain. It might not make things any better for you but could help the next woman in the same situation.

What I do remember is the kindness and ability of the midwife who delivered the baby.

The midwife was very supportive. I felt I had the intimacy of a home birth with the backup of hospital facilities.

I do feel strongly that in cases of epidural section the partner, if he is willing, should be allowed to be there. We asked and were told there was no room, yet six students were there. If they could be there, why not the father?

Choice of position

You may or may not have a choice of position for delivery, ranging from lying flat on your back in the lithotomy position to squatting in an upright position. It would be good if every woman could choose the position that suited her best, but this is possible only in a very few places. In this country the usual position for delivery is on your back or in the left lateral position — in this you lie on your side with your legs slightly bent and the top one raised and held. If these are the usual positions in your particular hospital and you would prefer something else, ask if it would be possible.

Lying flat on your back is not a very good position for birth, as you are pushing against gravity and reducing the blood supply to the uterus, though some midwives and doctors prefer to deliver women like this because they can see clearly what's happening. The lithotomy position, described previously — and also known as the "stranded beetle" position amongst women — is going out of favour, except for certain obstetrical interventions such as the rupture of the membranes. It is a most uncomfortable position and a number of women have remarked that they felt totally exposed and depersonalised when left like this for delivery. Luckily very few hospitals now use this position for birth. If you find it is the practice at your unit, ask if it is at least possible for your legs to be down on the table rather than up in the stirrups — perhaps your partner could help to hold them if necessary.

The worst part was having to lie on your back. It goes against gravity and human nature to be expected to push the baby out in these circumstances.

I wanted pillows to support my back but the nurses said I wouldn't be able to push so effectively if I sat up too much.

Routine dictated that I deliver in the supine position, whereas I felt instinctively I would have preferred to be more upright.

Many women find that the most comfortable position is a semi-sitting one, where they are propped up by pillows or supported by someone, perhaps their partner. This position still allows the medical staff to have a clear view of what is happening, gravity is assisting you as you push and you can, if you wish, actually see the baby being born.

Recently there have been some new ideas for delivery positions, although it would be more accurate to say they are old ideas that have been re-introduced, as they've been used by women around the world for thousands of years.

One is the supported squat, where the mother is upright during labour, and is held under the arms during each contraction, so that gravity can help the baby as much as possible during its descent. This method has received much publicity from its use by Dr. Michel Odent, an obstetrician from Pithiviers in France, who believes that many of the problems occurring in labour and during delivery are caused by modern intervention techniques. It is his policy not to interfere in labour (unless absolutely necessary) and he prefers the woman to use her own instincts to guide her during this time. You may also have read reports highlighting the fact that some babies delivered at Pithiviers are born in, or even under water — this is not a gimmick, but occurs because no drugs are ever used there for pain relief, and if a woman finds that the contractions are becoming very strong, she is invited to relax in a pool of warm water. Some choose to stay there to deliver — the baby comes to no harm because it has been surrounded by liquid for nine months in the womb — but the majority of women deliver from a squatting position on dry land.

A second idea is to give birth on all fours. As previously mentioned, some women who suffer a great deal of backache during labour find this position to be very helpful, because it literally tips the baby away from the mother's spine and thus eases the pressure on the back. In delivery it can help to rotate the baby's head from an awkward position to a better one for birth, but nevertheless this position is not very popular with the professionals and it is unlikely that you would be allowed to adopt this position.

Thirdly there is the birthing stool or chair, which has a horseshoe-shaped seat and usually arms or rails for the woman to hold onto. These can range from very simple wooden stools to very expensive models, like dentist's chairs with lifting and tilting mechanisms being incorporated, but in all of them the idea is that gravity is being employed. A number of hospitals in England employ these chairs, but so far only one hospital — the Coombe in Dublin — has purchased them.

The Rotunda in Dublin now has a birthing bed, working on the same principle of using gravity while supporting the mother, and it can be adapted from being an ordinary flat surface through various angles to provide upright support.

You may not, then, have very much choice as far as the delivery position is concerned, although there should not be any objection to the semi-sitting position for an ordinary birth. Certainly the supported squat is not widely encouraged, as many doctors and nurses feel that a major argument against it is that they cannot clearly see what is happening and thus intervene in an emergency; nevertheless one or two hospitals are now allowing women to deliver in this position if they wish.

120

The birthing chair was offered. I accepted with mixed feelings as I was used to the old methods. The nurses were marvellous, in spite of it being new to them, so encouraging. I recommend the chair, as I suffered from very cold, shivering legs. The back support is also good.

I squatted on the delivery bed. Midwives most accommodating.

I was encouraged to sit up and help deliver the baby — once the head was born I was shown how to slip my fingers under her armpits and deliver her myself.

Intervention in delivery

Whether or not your labour has been straightforward up to this point, there are two interventions which may take place at the time of delivery, and these are episiotomy and the use of forceps.

Episiotomy

An episiotomy is a cut made in the tissues of the perineum immediately below the entrance to the vagina, and is performed to enlarge the opening for the delivery of the baby's head. Obstetricians often say that a neat cut is preferable to a jagged tear which may occur naturally, as it can be repaired more neatly and efficiently, but there has been increasing debate as to whether many episiotomies need to be performed at all. In some hospitals about 80% of all first-time mothers receive episiotomies, yet in other units only about 10% of all mothers have one. Why should this be so?

If the delivery is unhurried, so that the perineal tissues can gently stretch and fan out, there is less likelihood that an episiotomy will be needed, and if you are told that one is to be performed, ask if a little more time can elapse before one is done. It may also help to move into a slightly more upright position, if this is allowed.

Of course, if the baby is in distress and you are told that an episiotomy is to be done, then naturally the baby must be delivered as quickly as possible; similarly if it is evident that the tissues will not stretch any further then you have an episiotomy, but it should not be done as a matter of routine.

If it is to be done, you should be given a local anaesthetic and then the tissues will be cut with surgical scissors. There are two kinds of incision: either midline, which is straight down from the vagina towards the anus, or medio-lateral, which is done at an angle down and sideways from the vagina. It will be the personal preference of the doctor or midwife that decides which you will have.

As with any surgical incision, an episiotomy will require stitching afterwards, and perhaps it is not so much the cut itself but stitching that attracts many complaints from women. The stitching ought to be done very carefully, not only because both muscles and skin will have been cut but because of the very sensitive nature of the perineal area itself, and can take up to an hour to repair. Silk or thread may be used, and will be removed on about the fourth or fifth day after delivery, though increasingly "dissolving" stitches are being used. You should be given a local anaesthetic and time should be allowed for this to take effect — a few doctors can be surprisingly insensitive about this, and if you do feel any pain when stitching begins, say so.

In any case there may be some discomfort afterwards, and warm baths can help to ease the soreness — you may also be advised to add some salt or gentle disinfectant such as Savlon to the water to speed the healing process. If this discomfort continues for any length of time, especially after you have left hospital, go and see your GP, as the stitches may have become infected and the site be in need of treatment. Sometimes, if the stitching has not been done as carefully as it ought there can be more serious and long-term problems, especially with intercourse. If you do have the misfortune to suffer long-term discomfort, do not be shy about going to your GP, as something should and can be done for you.

Nothing but a bit of soreness the first few days and then I was fine. Even to begin with a warm bath helped.

Sore for longer than I expected. I thought I was sewn too tightly and said so at my six week visit. The reply was "Better than too loose!"

My baby is now 4 months old. I have been unable to resume having sex. After several unsuccessful attempts I went to a GP. She says that I need to have my perineum cut and restitched. I felt this was the case ever since the baby was born. I will not ask the obstetrician to repair the damage he did. At my postnatal examination I reported soreness but he claimed everything was healing well and expressed surprise that I still felt sore. I am now seeking another doctor to repair my perineum.

Forceps delivery

Forceps may be used to deliver your baby for a variety of reasons, and you will almost certainly receive an episiotomy in these circumstances to allow easy delivery of the baby's head.

Obstetric forceps are made of fine steel blades which fit neatly round the baby's head, though there are a number of different shapes for different circumstances. A local anaesthetic is given to numb the area and then the forceps are applied to the baby's head. The forceps are pulled gently at short intervals until the crown of the head appears, when an episiotomy is done, and as soon as the head is delivered the forceps are removed. The rest of the baby is delivered spontaneously.

Forceps are used when delivery must be hurried up — if your blood pressure has risen a lot, for example, or if the baby is in distress, or if it is in an unusual position that requires help. If the baby is very premature, special forceps may be used to protect its head — the bones in this case are so soft that they could be badly mis-shapen by the passage through the birth canal, and the forceps actually protect the head during the expulsive stage of delivery.

If the second stage of labour is prolonged then the doctor may want to use forceps, but there is no standard definition of what a prolonged second stage is. Some doctors would say one that lasts for more than half an hour, while others might wait for an hour, or even longer, depending on whether the contractions are working usefully to push out the baby or not. Also, if you have had an epidural earlier on, you may still be unable to feel the contractions or respond to the bearing down sensations, in which case forceps will probably be necessary.

Ventouse delivery
An alternative to forceps is the ventouse or vacuum extractor, which can be used in certain circumstances by some doctors. The ventouse consists of a small metal cup which is placed against the baby's head with a tube attached to special equipment. It works on the same principle as a vacuum cleaner (though obviously not with the same force!) and gently pulls the baby down the birth canal. Because of the suction the baby will have a swelling on its head where the cup was applied, but this will quickly disappear after delivery.

Immediately after delivery
As long as the baby is perfectly well, you should be able to hold him as soon as he is born, if you want to. In many hospitals the baby is delivered on to your tummy before

the cord is cut, and you can put him to the breast straightaway.

Hospitals vary in their policies regarding cutting the umbilical cord. In some units it is clamped and cut as soon as the baby is delivered, but in others no division is made until the cord has stopped pulsing. The advantage of leaving the cord uncut is that the baby will receive the extra few ounces of blood draining from the placenta; indeed there is no necessity to cut the cord until the placenta is delivered though this will hardly happen in hospital. If the cord is round the baby's neck the division will probably be made immediately, though some doctors and midwives will just unloop the cord, if they can. In an emergency, of course, the cord will be clamped as quickly as possible.

My only complaint was that they cut the cord after delivery before it had quite stopped beating, though I asked them not to.

The midwife apologised for cutting the cord immediately, because it was round the baby's neck.

The placenta should be delivered fairly soon after the baby is born, though if there is any delay the doctor or midwife may exert gentle pressure on the cord while pressing your tummy. It is usual practice in this country to give the mother an injection to make the uterus contract after delivery to expel the placenta; this is done as the baby is being born and you may not even notice that it is being given.

The placenta is examined very carefully once it is delivered, as any small pieces remaining in the uterus must be removed before they can cause problems such as a post-partum haemorrhage. This is done by a simple "scrape" of the uterus under general anaesthetic. Similarly, if there is a problem with the expulsion of the placenta itself, you may have to have it removed surgically under a general anaesthetic.

Until fairly recently it was the practice in many hospitals that as soon as the baby was delivered he was taken by the midwife to have the mucus sucked from his airways, to be examined, washed, weighed, wrapped up tightly, perhaps shown to his mother and then placed in a warmed cot or incubator. Now more hospitals are recognising that for many women and their babies this is the very moment when they want and need to be together, and often the baby, having been delivered onto his mother's tummy, is simply wiped, wrapped warmly but loosely in a blanket and given straight to his mother. Doctors and midwives can assess the condition of the baby quite accurately as they deliver it, and unless there are any problems or life-threatening emergencies, a more detailed examination can wait until later.

The baby was left with me after delivery. The baby was wrapped only in a linen cloth and it was beautiful being left together for so long.

I asked that she be given to her dad who was outside the theatre, and this was done, and he held her until I was out of theatre.

When I asked if I could hold him I was told that the nurse was very busy, she had her notes to fill in as she was going off duty very soon.

I would have liked to hold the baby, but I even had to ask them four times whether it was a boy or a girl!

"Leboyer delivery"
This is probably the best place to mention the Leboyer style

126

of delivery. Leboyer is a French obstetrician (now retired from practice) who wrote *Birth without Violence*, in which he focuses on the baby's experience of birth, and argues that we should do everything to make that experience as gentle as possible. In order to do this the baby should be delivered into dim light and with as little noise as possible. He should be lifted gently and placed on the mother's bare tummy, where the parents can stroke him very gently. The cord should not be cut until it has finished pulsating. After a few minutes the baby should be placed in a nearby bath of warm water (to replace the environment he has just left in the womb) and then, wrapped in soft coverings, he should be laid on his side, alone, in his crib to begin to discover his new surroundings.

Dr. Leboyer concentrated totally on the baby, while many mothers would want to hold the baby straightaway, to cuddle it, to talk softly to it and to put it to the breast. In fact, what many parents mean when they ask for a "Leboyer" birth is the whole idea of "gentle birth" — as little fuss and noise as possible, no glaring lights, delivering the baby onto the mother's tummy and so on, but probably not the bath or leaving the baby alone is his cot.

Whether you want the "full" Leboyer or not, think about it during your pregnancy, discuss it with your doctor and get your requests written down. Some doctors dislike the mention of Leboyer because of his writings, which are quite emotive, but his basic philosophy is perfectly rational. There are one or two units which will do a "full" Leboyer delivery, including the warm bath, if that's what you want, but most would be more likely to go along with the ideas of a gentle, natural birth — no bright lights, delivering the baby onto your tummy, leaving the cord and so on.

The delivery was the only positive part of the experience, thanks to the midwife. *The beauty of the first sight and feel of the baby was not rushed over or destroyed.*

The midwives were very positive and encouraging and hubby, myself and baby were left undisturbed for an hour with a cup of tea — very humane and important to us.

Examination of the baby

As already mentioned, the doctor or midwife can estimate the newborn's condition quite well as delivery takes place. In fact, hospitals now use what is called the Apgar score to indicate the baby's state of health. It is named after the New York anaesthetist who developed this scoring system, and marks are given as shown below. The baby is "scored" approximately one minute after delivery and usually about five minutes later as well.

Score	0	1	2
Heart rate	Absent	Slow (below 100)	Above 100
Respiration	Absent	Slow, irregular	Good, crying
Muscle tone	Limp	Some flexion of extremities	Active
Reflexes	No responses	Grimace	Cry
Colour	Blue, pale	Body pink, extremities blue	Pink

An Apgar score of less than 7 indicates that something may be wrong, while a score between 4 and 0 indicates that the baby's life is in danger.

To the postnatal ward

After you have been cleaned up, stitched if necessary and the baby weighed, measured and examined, you may be left for a while in the delivery room, or go into a special post-labour room for a while, or you may go directly to the postnatal ward. At this time you should be offered some refreshment — tea and toast or something similar.

Your baby may or may not go back to the ward with you, depending on a number of circumstances. It may be hospital policy for all babies to be taken to the nursery for observation for some time, which can vary from one hour to twenty-four. Alternatively it may be policy that unless the baby requires special care, he automatically stays with his mother and goes back to the ward with her.

If you are delivered during the night, the staff may assume that you want to sleep and therefore take the baby to the nursery till the morning. Of course, after all the hard work of labour you are perfectly entitled to a good night's sleep and hopefully that is what you will get, but many women find that after delivery they are excited and on a "high", so that sleep is impossible and they just want to have the baby with them. If you want to keep the baby with you, say so. Ask politely, saying that you'll rest better knowing the baby is there beside you. If they insist on taking the baby to the nursery, emphasise that you want him to be brought to you when he wakes for feeding (if this is what you want).

SECTION FOUR

After Birth

15

In Hospital

*I actually enjoyed my stay in hospital and have nothing but
praise for conditions, food, staff, help with breastfeeding, advice
on how to cope with the baby, etc.*

I had first class treatment and thoroughly enjoyed it all.

After delivery you will be taken to a postnatal ward, or
to your room if you are a private patient. As already
mentioned, you may not be able to have a room
straightaway, but you should be given one as soon as it
becomes vacant.

Also previously mentioned is the fact that hospitals vary
in their policies about mothers and babies being together.
In some units your baby stays with you day and night unless
you wish otherwise, while in others it depends on the
numbers of beds in the ward, the other mothers' attitudes
and so on. A third variation is that your baby stays with
you all day but has to go to the nursery at night (and
possibly during visiting hours as well), while in a very few
units you can only have your baby at the routine feeding
times, usually every four hours. Very few women like this
latter situation, and it certainly does nothing to promote
successful breastfeeding. If you are in a room on your own
it should be possible to have the baby with you all the time,
if you so wish, though many women prefer the baby to
be in the nursery at night. If you are in a ward you may

not be able to have the baby with you as much as you would like — see the section on feeding for more about this.

I would have preferred her with me at night, but as I was in a ward with five others it might not have been practical.

I could have had her all the time if I had wanted but I was tired and slept better feeling she was being looked after, as I didn't feel confident or competent.

I enjoyed the rest and the freedom of getting to know my new baby.

I had to insist on having the baby with me all the time. They thought I was mad.

Ward routine
If this is the first time that you've been in hospital you may be quite amazed at the way time can pass during the day.

You were woken at six, then just as you were getting back to sleep you were asked if you wanted breakfast. There was always something and I never got enough sleep.

You will probably be woken up quite early, perhaps between six and seven, for a cup of tea and to feed the baby and change him as well. Incidentally, if you are in your own room and have the baby with you anyway, you may prefer to sleep on, so ask the nurses if this would be possible. It might not be, but you can always ask! If you are in a ward, of course, you will be woken up along with everyone else. After this early start there may be a bit of a lull while the nurses change shift, so depending on how you feel you could take the opportunity for another quick nap, or perhaps take a bath or shower.

The bathroom arrangements do, unfortunately, come in for a lot of criticism, especially in the larger hospitals, on the grounds of hygiene and overcrowding. With so many women using the facilities cleanliness can be something of a problem, and you should bring any serious defects to the attention of the staff. You may, by the way, find it useful to take your own roll of toilet paper with you — it is supplied, of course, but it can disappear very quickly and catch you out.

As far as the overcrowding is concerned, many hospitals have been catering for far more patients than they were ever designed for, and consequently it may not always be possible to take a bath or shower whenever you want one. If you have had stitches, a warm bath can really help to relieve the discomfort, so ask when the best times are to use the bathrooms.

As there were over fifty patients to one bathroom, I was lucky to get a bath when I did.

The baths are very difficult to get into. To sit down was just painful. Surely a split level idea, and bidets, should be standard in maternity units. Obviously they were all designed by men.

It is not a reflection on staff but rather on facilities and overcrowding to say that hygiene and general cleanliness are appalling. One bath and only two toilets, often clogged, wet and bloody towels — ugh!

While on the subject of hygiene, remember that you will be wearing thick sanitary pads, even if you normally use tampons. The pads can be kept in place by a sanitary belt, but you may prefer to use disposable briefs which are available in chemists' shops. These keep the pads securely place and can then be thrown away after use.

Incidentally, hospitals are very hot places — the temperature is kept artificially high in maternity units to keep the babies warm — and you may feel more comfortable in a short-sleeved cotton nightdress. Nylon and flannelette can make you feel terribly sticky in such heat, even in the depths of winter.

To return to ward routine — your mornings will probably be taken up with breakfast, more feeding and changing, bathing the baby (though this may be done for you), visits from the ward sister, matron, the doctor, nurses taking your temperature and blood pressure and making your bed, plus cleaners, newspaper sellers and so on. There are, of course, times when nothing much will be happening and the baby will be fast asleep, so, like the ante-natal clinic, go in prepared — take your knitting, or a new book to read, or catch up on letters you have to write. Alternatively you can always close your eyes and go back to sleep!

Neon lights on overhead from 6 a.m. to 11 p.m. and a continuous stream of health personnel, cups of tea, etc.

I had too much to do. Had expected to have more time to relax, to be taken care of.

Incidentally, you may be surprised how quickly you will be up and out of bed after delivery. Gone are the days when a mother had to stay in bed for at least a week under threat of permanently ruining her health! Unless there are medical reasons against it, you will be out of bed and walking around as soon as possible, usually within twelve hours of delivery and certainly within twenty-four. This movement helps to restore your circulation and prevents constipation, so do make the effort to walk around a little as soon as you can, even if your stitches are sore.

You may also receive a visit from the physiotherapist who will tell you how to do your postnatal exercises, or there may be a class for them at certain times. Get started on the exercises straightaway, especially the ones designed to tone up the pelvic muscles. It's very easy to promise yourself that you will do them tomorrow, but as we all know, tomorrow never comes!

There may also be mothercraft classes, or demonstrations of how to bath a baby and so on, and you may like to go along to these, especially if this is your first baby. Alternatively every mother may be given an individual lesson by the nurse.

Food

Since your day will be punctuated at regular intervals by meals, it might be as well to introduce the topic of hospital food.

In theory your diet at this time should be high in roughage, or fibre as it's more popularly known now, to encourage your bowels to work normally again, and especially for those who are breastfeeding the diet should be very nourishing. However, many women find that hospital food is far too bland and even greasy: there may be lots of fried foods, white bread, sweet puddings and very little fresh fruit or vegetables.

Hospital dieticians say that they are aware of the problem, but that within a limited budget they have to do their best by catering for majority tastes, otherwise they'll be faced with large amounts of wasted foods. Getting people used to eating better kinds of food is a long-term approach, but two simple changes would be to substitute whole-grain brown bread for the white loaves and to offer fresh fruit instead of sticky puddings.

You can do several things for yourself, though, if you feel that the food needs improvement. Take in, or get someone to bring you a small packet of bran and sprinkle it on whatever cereal is provided for breakfast. (You could also chop up an apple or a banana to go with it). If there is a choice of menus, go for the salads or less fatty, higher protein foods such as chicken rather than the fries all the time — though one fried meal won't do you any harm if you suddenly have a passionate longing for fish and chips! Ask visitors to bring you fresh fruit and, especially if you're breastfeeding and find that you need to step up your liquid intake, ask for fruit juices rather than the heavily sweetened cordial drinks. If you do become constipated then ask the nurse for a laxative, but it's much better if you can get your bowels moving again naturally.

If you are a vegetarian, or require any other special diet, remember to have this written in your notes at an ante-natal visit, and also tell a nurse or the ward sister when you get to the ward.

Awful — stodgy — no fresh fruit or vegetables.

I was always hungry. We were given packet soup, greasy fries and rhubarb. No bran or brown bread available.

The food was atrocious. Not a bit of fibre in sight. All stodge and horrendous boiled bacon or sausage. Vegetables inedible, no fresh fruit or salad. Cornflakes with the milk poured on half an hour before breakfast. You'd think they'd make sure postpartum mothers get plenty of fibre — nutritionists how are ye!

The food is nice, appetising and nutritious. I was in over Christmas and a lot of effort went into the catering.

The food was excellent and beautifully prepared. I especially liked the home-made brown bread!

Top marks to the nutritionists. Meals were varied, well

presented and tasty, although there was a lack of fresh fruit. Salads and brown bread were plentiful.

Smoking

One aspect of hospital life that should be mentioned is the question of smoking. At best smoking is an anti-social habit and at its worst a killer. You will have read in an earlier chapter that mothers who smoke in pregnancy can affect their babies, because the harmful nicotine from the cigarettes passes through the placenta to the baby.

If mothers and visitors are allowed to smoke in the postnatal ward, then the air is polluted for everyone, newborn babies included, and yet some hospitals seem more reluctant than others to tackle this problem. Notices can be put up telling people not to smoke, but they are useless if they are not reinforced by telling offenders to stop. The best solution is to ban smoking altogether in the wards and to have a room set aside for those who must smoke (not the day room, because then non-smokers would still be passive recipients of the smoke). Some hospitals have already instituted such a policy, and the new anti-smoking legislation which is due shortly may force the others to do something. At the moment some hospitals have "smoking" and "non-smoking" wards, which is better than nothing for the mothers but doesn't protect the babies in the former.

If you are persistently bothered by people smoking, tell the ward sister, matron and the doctor, as you should be entitled to unpolluted air, especially in a hospital of all places! Once you get home, write to the Master or senior consultant and the matron with your views on this, as until the law can be used, only consumer pressure can bring about change.

I wanted a semi-private room but moved to a private room

because the other patients were all smoking which I didn't think was good for the babies.

I got very upset during my stay about the amount of smoking allowed on the ward. There were "No Smoking" signs, but the nurses never said a word even to mothers smoking while feeding their babies or to the many visitors smoking in our room.

Visiting hours
Visiting hours will vary from one hospital to another, but usually there is at least an hour in the afternoon and another hour in the evening. Some units allow fairly unrestricted visiting by partners. If times are strictly adhered to but your partner has difficulty in visiting you at that particular time — perhaps because of shift-work, for example — ask the ward sister if other arrangements can be made.

Only one hour in the afternoon and half-an-hour in the evening — not suitable for country areas.

I was in an annexe — lovely relaxed atmosphere with visitors allowed all day and children encouraged also.

Hospitals also vary in their policies regarding children visiting the wards. It is now recognised that for a young child to have his mother disappear at short notice, possibly in the middle of night and to reappear a week later with a new baby can be very upsetting, regardless of how well prepared he has been for the new arrival. Some hospitals, therefore, have begun to allow brothers and sisters to visit, though others do not. They may be able to come in every day, which is quite satisfactory, or only one or two days may be set aside for them. This is certainly a start in the right direction but may be of no use to you and your family

— if children can only visit on Saturday afternoons, for example, and you are delivered at Saturday tea-time, you'll probably be home before the next children's visiting time.

Children used to be excluded on the grounds of the possibility of infections being passed to new babies, but by and large this has been discarded as a reason — though in all fairness children who are ill or even suffering from a cold should not be brought in.

If you're in a private hospital or nursing home visiting is usually much less restricted. You will probably be allowed to have visitors for most of the day, and children are usually allowed in too. Whether you're in a private room or not, too many visitors can be tiring and if you really feel you cannot face any more, tell your partner to pass the word around and also have a word with the ward sister. She may be able to restrict your visitors or at least keep them to the minimum of time. Don't worry about offending people — your rest is more important at a time like this.

Phones will be available for you to make and receive personal calls. In all but one or two nursing homes you will have to use a call box, so make sure that you have some change and that anyone who is likely to ring you knows the number.

No children allowed — why is this? Found it very distressing not to see my other children.

Very liberal visiting. Children are allowed to visit, no problem. Husbands can visit any time.

Religious services

If you are a Catholic you will find that Mass is celebrated regularly even if the hospital does not have a chapel — day rooms or lecture theatres may be used instead. If for any reason you are unable to attend Mass, Holy Communion can be brought to you. Confessions can also be heard, and if you wish to see a priest at any time, ask one of the nurses what the arrangements are.

Ministers of the other major denominations will usually visit on a regular basis, and again you should ask the staff if you wish to see one.

Under certain circumstances your baby may be baptised while you are still in hospital. The ward sister will talk to you about this and tell you about the arrangements. (See also chapter 17)

Medication

If you have been taking iron and/or vitamin tablets during your pregnancy you should continue to do so now, unless the doctor tells you otherwise. If you were not taking iron tablets beforehand, ask if you should take them now, as you will be losing a fair amount of your body's store of iron in the blood loss after delivery.

If you have been taking any other medication during pregnancy (for example, for diabetes or for high blood pressure), check with the doctor whether you should continue to do so and/or if the dosage needs to be changed.

Should your stitches be causing you discomfort, you can ask for a mild pain reliever such as panadol. Similarly, you may have some discomfort from after-pains, which are like mild contractions and occur as the uterus continues to shrink back down to its normal size. These sensations may be especially noticeable when the baby is feeding at the breast and for some reason are stronger with second or subsequent babies. Again, if you are in more than temporary discomfort, ask for a mild pain reliever.

It may be difficult to sleep at night, especially if you are in a large ward with other women all around you. Even in your own room there will probably be people passing up and down the corridor during the night, phones ringing, and if your baby is in the nursery against your wishes you may not relax for imagining him to be crying. First of all try to relax — easier said than done, but use the techniques you learned for labour, and if it's the thought of the baby keeping you awake, go down to the nursery and have a look at your baby. The staff may think you're mad, but it's better that you can see him sleeping (or do something about it if he's not) so that you can rest. If you are having trouble sleeping (apart from the first night after delivery when many women find they are on a "high" from all the excitement) then ask for a mild sleeping tablet. One isn't going to turn you into an addict!

It was impossible to get a reasonable amount of sleep.

I definitely think it's terrible to be awakened at 5.30 a.m. and there was no rest whatsoever. I felt I would get more rest at home.

I had to spend the first night in a big ward and got hardly any sleep, what with the snoring and a couple of new mothers being brought in. It was lovely to get into my own room and shut out all the noise and bustle.

Rhesus mothers
The subject of the rhesus factor is quite complicated and you may like to read about it in more detail in one of the more medical books about pregnancy.

It is sufficient to say here that your blood will have been tested during one of your earliest ante-natal visits and if, like the majority of the population you are found to have what is called the Rhesus factor you are one of those with a Rhesus positive (Rh+ for short) blood group. If the factor is missing, you are Rhesus negative (Rh- for short). If you are Rh+ then there are no problems, and even if you are Rh- it will not cause any problems if your partner is also Rh-, or Rh+ but of a different blood group.

Problems may arise if both you and your partner have the same blood group and he is Rh+ and you are Rh-. Your baby may then be either Rh+ or Rh-, and again, if he is Rh- there is no problem. If, however, the baby is Rh+, during the pregnancy and delivery some of his blood cells may escape into your circulation and sensitise you. This means that if in future more Rh+ cells enter your body (during your next pregnancy, for example), your defence system will begin to destroy them. This could eventually lead to the foetus in the next pregnancy suffering from certain conditions or possibly even death.

Fortunately science has come to our aid, and this is one application for which we should be wholeheartedly thankful. It was discovered that if these Rh- mothers who bore an Rh+ baby were given an antibody shortly after delivery, any Rh+ cells in her body would be destroyed before she was sensitised by them. If you are Rh-, therefore, a sample of your baby's blood (from the cord) will be tested shortly after delivery, and if he is Rh+ you will be given an injection of a substance called anti-D immunoglobulin within a day or so of the birth. This is completely painless but protects you and any future children.

During future pregnancies your blood will be tested regularly to make sure that the baby is in no danger of rhesus disease. If necessary the baby can be given a blood transfusion immediately after delivery or even, thanks again to science, a transfusion can be given while the baby is still in the womb. This is a highly complex procedure and would be fully explained to you beforehand, but it is becoming a much rarer occurrence now that the problem can be treated simply and effectively after the first and subsequent pregnancies.

Section mothers

After a section you will naturally have some pain from your scar, and pain relievers can be given to help with this. You will be encouraged to move your legs about in bed to help your circulation, and to cough up any phlegm or mucus. Within 24 hours you will be encouraged to get out of bed to use the toilet and clean your teeth, etc. You should be drinking normally by this time, and by the second day you will probably be sitting up to eat your meals and be feeding your baby. (See Chapter 16 for more about feeding after a section).

The doctor will remove your stitches on about the fifth day after delivery, provided that the scar is healing well. If the area has been feeling tight and itchy it will probably be much better once the stitches are out, and you can also bathe or shower as normal.

Most women who have had sections are kept in hospital for about ten days — it is major abdominal surgery, after all, though occasionally you will stay longer if there are any complications.

"Blues"

Postnatal depression is discussed more fully in the final chapter, but it should be mentioned here that in the first few days after delivery you may well experience what's often known as the "blues". This is an emotional reaction to an incredible happening and you're not at all unusual to experience it. Your body has been through a tremendous upheaval and your hormones are in imbalance at this time as well, so it's not surprising that you feel some reaction. You may burst into tears at the slightest thing, you may wish that you'd never had the baby or you may wonder how you'll ever cope. In fact, a good cry may be the best thing for you by relieving all that pent-up tension, but the main thing is to be forewarned that it might happen and that it will, in the majority of cases, soon pass.

Incidentally, don't expect to feel great outpourings of love for your baby immediately he's born. Sometimes you will experience love at first sight, just as men and women do occasionally in adult life, but like a lot of other relationships you may find that your affection for the child develops quite slowly. So don't feel guilty or abnormal about any absence of deep love straightaway.

It was a very emotional time for all of us in the ward and the hospital system doesn't seem able to take this into consideration.

When found cuddling the baby, I was warned of the risks of "over-handling" a baby. As for having my baby in bed with me — this is the cardinal sin! I can laugh about it now, but at the time I cried. Does nobody other than mothers and fathers understand that we love our babies?

Your baby in hospital
Your baby will be the focus of attention not only for you and your visitors but for various other people as well.

As mentioned in the chapter on delivery, he will be examined at birth for any obvious problems and is given an Apgar score. Within a day or two he will be very carefully examined by a paediatrician (a doctor who specialises in the care of young children). He will check the "tone" of the baby and whether the baby has a gripping reflex when his hand is touched. There are several ways that the doctor can estimate whether the baby was born early, or late, or at the right time. For example, a premature baby will have hardly any markings on the soles of his feet, while the more mature a baby the deeper these wrinkles will be. Similarly the amount of fine hair on the baby's body can help to estimate his age — in premature babies it is still often present all over the back, while on mature babies it will be seen only on the lower half of the back. The paediatrician will also check the baby's heart, lungs, reflexes and genitals. In many hospitals this examination is done with the mother present, so that everything can be explained to her. Whether you see the examination being done or not, ask the paediatrician if you have any worries about the baby.

Your baby will also be weighed regularly in hospital, probably every day or every other day. Remember that all babies lose some weight to begin with, but should be starting to regain it by the end of the first week.

On or about the fourth day after birth your baby will be given its PKU test. These initials are short for phenylketonuria, a disease which if left undetected and untreated can cause mental retardation in later years. If the PKU test proves positive a special diet will be prescribed which is fully effective in preventing the development of this disease. The PKU test is done by pricking the baby's heel and taking some drops of blood onto specially treated paper. Your baby will probably cry at this, but just give him a cuddle afterwards! It is also possible for the test to be done with a urine sample, but naturally this is rather harder to do with small babies.

If you live in or give birth in a hospital in a large urban area, your baby will also be given BCG vaccination, which prevents the development of tuberculosis (TB). If your baby does not receive his vaccination in hospital, either because the particular hospital does not offer it or because of some medical reason (low birth weight, for example), you should be able to get his BCG done at a health clinic near your home. Enquire at your nearest clinic, or ask the public health nurse or your GP.

You will also have to register the birth and usually the hospital will do this for you. They will require the parents' names, address, father's occupation, the date of marriage (if applicable) and the baby's chosen names and date of birth. Alternatively you can or may have to register the birth yourself — the hospital will give you details. Birth certificates take some weeks to be issued and you will be given details of how and where to apply for them.

Going home

Unless you have arranged to go home early you will probably stay in hospital for about five days. The length of stay will depend on several things — whether it is your first baby or not, whether you are breast or bottle feeding, and how much pressure there is on the accommodation in the hospital. Occasionally hospitals have to discharge mothers a day earlier than usual simply because they need the beds, though with the falling birth rate this is not so much of a problem as it used to be. You should also note that unless there is a medical reason for a longer stay (including a section) the VHI will only reimburse costs for five days.

If you have had a section, you will of course stay longer in hospital. The usual length of stay is between ten and fourteen days, unless complications mean you require a longer stay.

Both you and the baby will be given final examinations before you go home, and you will be told when and where to return for your postnatal checkup and the baby's six-week examination.

My ideal would have been to have the baby in hospital but return home immediately afterwards.

I had nobody at home to help me and in hospital I still felt that the responsibility wasn't mine yet. I was afraid to be totally responsible for my tiny baby.

Don't forget that if the baby has been wearing hospital clothes since he was born, he will need clothes to go home in. If you don't take them in with you, ask your partner or someone else to bring them in. You should dress him in a vest and something like a babygro, and then something on top to keep him warm — a jacket, or a shawl or blanket would be suitable, but make sure that his head is covered, especially if the weather is cold.

If for any reason you want to go home earlier than usual this may or may not be encouraged (see chapter 4 for more discussion about this). If you are a first-time mother then the hospital will probably want you to stay in for whatever is the standard length of time of four to six days, while if you have had your second or subsequent baby they are more likely to let you go, providing that there is someone at home to look after you. If the worst comes to the worst you can discharge yourself and the baby, but be warned that this will be a very unpopular move. You may even be asked to sign a form saying something to the effect that the hospital undertakes no further responsibility for you or the baby and that if anything happens they will not be held accountable. Hopefully you will not be driven to this position — if anything is making you desperately unhappy, talk to your partner, or to the ward sister or the doctor to see if something can be done. The trend is towards more flexibility in the length of stay, though as we shall see in a later chapter, there are definitely not the back-up services that should really be provided for newly discharged mothers in this country.

I only stayed one day. I felt if I had to stay another day I would have got very depressed and upset as I find hospital routine very tiring and depressing.

I felt confident with the baby by the time I left. Earlier I think I'd have been nervous with her.

16

Feeding the Baby

Although this chapter has been included in the postnatal section, you should really think about feeding during your pregnancy. You will then be able to read as much as you can about the subject and decide what is going to be best for you and your baby. In any case this chapter does not attempt to deal with much beyond the basic practicalities, and for detailed advice and information you should consult some of the books on the subject (see Appendix 2) and/or get in touch with one of the organisations mentioned below.

Breast or bottle?

Your first decision will be whether you are going to breastfeed or bottle feed, unless you are one of the very few mothers for whom there is a genuine medical reason against breastfeeding. Examples of this would be mothers taking certain drugs such as cytotoxins (anti-cancer drugs) and steroids. Your doctor will in any case advise you in these circumstances.

Otherwise the decision must be yours and yours alone. As the saying goes, breast is best and no one can deny it. There are many advantages in breastfeeding: breast milk is the baby's natural food, there is no danger of contamination, it is always at the right temperature and there is no preparation involved. Breastfeeding aids the involution (shrinking) of the uterus back to normal after delivery, and can provide a degree of contraception during

150

the early weeks (though you shouldn't rely on it as being totally foolproof). Also, some women simply enjoy the sensation of suckling their babies, both physically and emotionally.

Most natural, healthiest, most convenient.

Breasts are there to make milk for babies, aren't they?

Apart from the knowledge that it's the best it just seemed so natural.

It took hours of very patient and confident help from the nurse to establish breastfeeding. Bottle feeding seemed much easier and less painful and the advantages of breastfeeding are not apparent until long after one has left hospital.

Having said all this, there is no point in attempting to breastfeed your baby if you find the idea absolutely disgusting. It is unfortunate that in our culture breasts are seen as sexual objects to be used more often for male titillation and in advertising than as the means of nourishing babies, and this can sometimes be unconsciously imbibed by impressionable young girls and women, so they somehow feel that anything to do with that part of their anatomy is rather shameful. Also, because for a time bottle feeding was seen as superior — since only the rich could afford all the equipment — almost whole generations have been bottle fed, with the result that many women have never been used to the sight of the baby at the breast in perhaps the way our mothers and grandmothers were, and this may reinforce any negative feelings about breastfeeding. This is not to say that all women who bottle feed feel like this — there are many different reasons — but it may be there subconsciously.

Anyway, it is probably better for a baby to be bottlefed by a relaxed mother than for a nervous, worrying mother to attempt breastfeeding — this can inhibit the milk flow, make the baby tense, start a vicious circle and generally cause all kinds of problems. However, if you are undecided, remember that you can always start off by breastfeeding and then switch to a bottle if you want to, but only in the rarest of situations could you do it the other way around. Even a few days of breastfeeding will give your baby the benefit of the protein-laden and antibody-rich colostrum — this is the yellowish substance that is secreted from the breasts before the true milk comes in. Ideally you should at least try to breastfeed, but if you do decide against it, don't feel guilty or worried — just get on with enjoying your baby!

I would feel too tied to breastfeeding.

I have a dislike even for the thought of breastfeeding.

I had bottlefed the other two and didn't want to change; my husband enjoys feeding the baby as well.

I just do not have the desire to breastfeed. I find the idea very messy!

Breastfeeding

If you have decided to breastfeed, the best preparation you can do is to learn as much as possible about it during pregnancy. Have a look at some of the books on the subject. Obviously theory and practice are two different things, but you should pick up a lot of advice that will get you off to a good start and you'll know where to turn for advice should any difficulties arise.

Unfortunately little advice seems to be forthcoming

during the formal part of ante-natal care — very few doctors seem to know anything about breastfeeding or are prepared to actively encourage it. Even the ante-natal clinics are not used as much as they could be for giving information and encouragement, so for those women who don't attend classes as well, no advice may be available.

I never thought of breastfeeding. Now I would have liked to, but nobody ever really talked to me about it.

I was given advice, at the hospital, by appointment during my fifth month — it concerned breast care and preparation.

I am of small build with a 32" bust, and as the child weighed 9 lbs I was advised against feeding. I went on to feed that child for nine months!

Without books I wouldn't have succeeded.

Good ante-natal classes should include some discussion and information on breastfeeding. Occasionally there are complaints that a few hospital classes have been rather dismissive on the subject, with bottle feeding receiving far greater attention. This should be changing now that there's far greater emphasis on the benefits of breastfeeding, but if you feel that you don't get enough advice, or that sufficient attention is not being paid to the subject, then tell the teacher — this may help women in later classes — and go back to the books on the subject.

On a practical note you should wear well-supporting bras during pregnancy, whether you are going to breastfeed or not, as your breasts will increase in size quite a lot. If you are going to breastfeed, some of the special nursing bras can be worn during pregnancy as well. One kind of bra has a drop-down panel on each cup, and another has cups which unhook independently on each side. A third kind (the Mava bra) unhooks and also laces up the back to accommodate your changing sizes, and is available by mail order from the National Childbirth Trust in England. The other two kinds are available in a number of outlets such as department stores, shops selling maternity wear and lingerie shops, and also by mail order from Mothercare.

Special nightdresses designed to make breastfeeding easier can also be obtained from the same sources. You may think that front-opening nighties will be suitable, though to be quite honest some of them don't open down far enough, and they do leave you feeling rather exposed — you might not mind when you're home but in the middle of a busy ward you might wish to be more discreet. The special nightdresses have two concealed slits at the front and allow you to breastfeed without baring the whole breast.

Also, think about your wardrobe in general. Separates are obviously the best clothes for easier breastfeeding; many front-opening dresses aren't really suitable, because, like the nightdresses mentioned above, many don't open far enough and you will be exposed to public view. It may not bother you but for various reasons the sight of a baby at the breast upsets a lot of people in this country and they may even make objections about it. This says a lot about *their* attitudes and hang-ups, but nevertheless, if you can be discreet, do!

Helpful organisations
There are two organisations which can help you with preparation for breastfeeding and with support and advice when the baby arrives.

The first is La Leche League (LLL) which has groups in many parts of the country. Their meetings are not classes but rather groups of mothers sharing information about breastfeeding and related aspects of birth and childcare. Meetings are held once a month, with a different theme each time, and the group leaders are mothers who have successfully fed at least one and usually two babies for some length of time. Any mother or mother-to-be is welcome to attend, or to call for advice at any time.

The second organisation is the Irish Childbirth Trust's Breastfeeding Support Group. ICT breastfeeding counsellors are also mothers who have breastfed their babies, and they give practical help and moral support on a mother-to-mother basis. It's not necessary to be attending ICT ante-natal classes or even to be involved with the ICT to approach their counsellors: you are free to seek advice and help at any time.

Both organisations offer constant contact, and they both publish leaflets on breastfeeding which are available by post.

It must be emphasised that neither group tries to replace medical advice, but rather aims to supplement professional help. If a medical problem arises they will always refer you back to your doctor. Their great advantages lie in the fact that the leaders and counsellors are all women who have breastfed their own babies and know exactly what breastfeeding involves. They too have been through the days of doing nothing but feeding the baby, the milk seeping out onto clothes, the breasts heavy with milk, the baby who won't latch on properly — and they've been through all the good moments too! They are always available to lend a listening ear, and this is especially valuable at the time when professional workers are off duty. These mothers have made a voluntary commitment to supporting breastfeeding mothers, and you should never worry that they will turn you away or refuse to listen to you.

There was a nurse responsible for breastfeeding but she never came near me after hearing I had attended a few meetings with

La Leche League. It seems to me the medical profession often feel threatened by the mothers who run this wonderful association of support and information.

My doctor actually gave me a leaflet about LLL during one of my ante-natal visits. I never got in touch with them at the time but I was glad of their help when I ran into problems after the birth.

I got tremendous support from the ICT and their breastfeeding counsellor.

Breastfeeding in hospital

Once the baby is born you may be able to put him to the breast immediately. If the baby sucks at this time it actually encourages the uterus to contract down and expel the placenta, though many babies aren't very interested in sucking straightaway. They often just lick or nuzzle the breast to begin with. About fifteen or twenty minutes later they are usually more eager to suck, so it's a great advantage to have the baby with you continuously after delivery.

Some hospitals do not allow the baby to stay with his mother but take him to the nursery for "observation", and in some units a solution of glucose and water is given to all breastfed babies by a bottle before feeding proper begins. One of the reasons behind this was to establish that there are no obstructions in the digestive tract, and the other was to encourage the passage of the meconium — this is the thick, sticky greenish-black stuff which the baby passes before the normals stools are formed. Neither of these reasons really justify feeding a baby such sweet fluid, but if the staff insist that the baby has to have something, ask them to give him plain boiled water. Some units also insist that all babies have the glucose solution at each feed, but there is absolutely no necessity for this and you should not give it to your baby if you don't want to.

One major problem that militates against the establishment of successful breastfeeding is the insistence in some hospitals on a rigid feeding routine. It's amazing that in the very place where you should be getting the maximum help and support you are sometimes made to feel that you are spoiling your newborn for life simply because his feeding requirements don't fit into the hospital routine. For many years hospitals have worked on a four-hourly feeding routine — babies were fed on the dot at two, six, ten, two, six and so on right round the clock, until these times seem to have been engraved on tablets of stone as absolute commandments! In all fairness many bottle-fed babies do in fact last about four hours between feeds — cow's milk, being meant for calves, takes longer to digest than breast milk and therefore remains longer in the stomach. Most breastfed babies, though, will only go a maximum of three hours to begin with, and of course this will not fit if the hospital has a four-hour routine. In any case some mothers like to feed "on demand", whenever the baby wants to suck, and this can be very frequently indeed in the first few weeks — tiny babies often suck for a few minutes and then drop off to sleep, waking in an hour or so for another snack.

You should decide which you're happier doing — some women like to have a routine to keep to, while others prefer to fit in with the baby's needs. If you like a routine, tell the nurses that you want to feed every three hours and see if the baby is happy with this. He may, of course, go the full four hours, but as many breastfed babies don't, yours isn't unnatural or underfed if he wants more frequent feeds!

With all three babies it has been a source of puzzlement to me as to how incongruous medical practice can sometimes be. Whilst advocating natural feeding (which to their credit

157

hospitals do seem to be making efforts to do now) they hammer home the necessity of unnatural feeding times with an enforced timetable.

Despite demand feeding the nurses still had to keep a record of the number of feeds per side per day — I found they had concocted a mythical feeding schedule which I had in no way adhered to.

Demand feeding would have made the establishment of breastfeeding much easier. The nurses frowned on any deviation from the timetable.

Breastfeeding is actively encouraged and demand feeding truly exists (not just in name as in so many places).

Some hospitals simply don't like the idea of demand feeding, and you may find it quite difficult if you're in a ward with staff constantly around you and possibly with many of the mothers bottle feeding. The only advice in these circumstances is to stick to your ideas firmly but politely and maybe to go home as soon as possible (all other things being equal) because then it'll be easier to do things your way. If you're in a room on your own there shouldn't be any problem, but if you are criticised, just tell the staff as calmly as you can that you feel happier this way, and remind them of the law of supply and demand — frequent sucking encourages the milk supply to come in. Luckily more hospitals are now accepting the idea of demand feeding, so you may not run into any problems at all, at least during the day.

I strongly object to nursing mothers being sent away to a special room to breastfeed their babies because of what visitors to the ward might think. Not even screens as a compromise! Staff did not have either adequate or correct information about breastfeeding, and although they professed "breast is best" they lacked knowledge, encouragement and sympathy to promote it. Their system, which is pretty well enforced on one, with schedules and supplements, is damaging to breastfeeding.

Though the hospital attitude is in favour of breastfeeding I found this was not always the case "on the ground". Some staff were encouraging and supportive but others were destructive and negative and comments like "You should know all about this before you come in here" and "It's O.K. if it works" do not inspire confidence.

At night

If the baby stays with you all the time, there should be no problem about feeding him during the night, as you can just pick him up when he wakes. You can keep his cot right by your bed, if you wish, so you'll hardly be disturbed at all.

The biggest problem may occur if your baby is taken to the nursery for the night, as happens in the majority of units, and yet you wish to feed him during that time. You can ask the nurses to wake you if he wakes for a feed, but sometimes they are reluctant to do so, mainly from misguided kindness — they feel that you need your night's sleep and that a couple of bottles won't harm your baby. This in fact is all wrong. For one thing your milk supply will be better if your breasts are emptied at regular intervals, and secondly, if you go for long periods — such as overnight — without feeding the baby, you are more likely to suffer from engorged breasts. This means that because the breasts are full of milk the pressure builds up, they can become very heavy and hot and can be very painful. Also, just one feed of cow's milk can sensitise a child who has an allergy to it and lead to all sorts of problems later on. So tell the nurses that you really do want to feed the baby at night

— after all, it's less work for them! — and that you'll go down to the nursery, if necessary, to save disturbing the other women in the ward. Pin a note to the baby's blanket saying "To be breastfed only" when he goes to the nursery, and if this doesn't work, have a word with the ward sister or the doctor. Of course, many hospitals have a very positive attitude towards breastfeeding and refuse to give a bottle without the mother's permission, which is excellent; in these cases you can rely on your baby getting only your milk.

Of course, if you prefer your baby to go to the nursery at night so that you can sleep undisturbed this should present no problems as far as accommodating your wishes is concerned. Do be aware though, that to begin with it is preferable, just for your own sake, to feed the baby at least once during the night to encourage the milk supply and prevent engorgement.

As I was breastfeeding I think it would have been preferable to have the baby all the time, day and night.

I kept the baby in bed with me at night, which was a great help in breastfeeding, and it meant I got a good night's sleep. The sister said how cosy we looked!

What help will there be in hospital?
The help given to breastfeeding mothers varies from hospital to hospital and even from ward to ward within a hospital, which is why it's a good idea to have had some advice beforehand or to have done some reading. Otherwise you may end up getting different advice every time the shift changes, and to be quite honest, many of the younger nurses can only tell you what they've learned from their textbooks, whereas the senior staff may either have

breastfed their own children or have had years of experience helping mothers.

The Coombe Hospital in Dublin has had the excellent idea of appointing two nursing sisters whose job is to work specifically on establishing feeding (either breast or bottle) and they will go out of their way to encourage breastfeeding. Reports from mothers have indicated that they like this system, because the advice is consistent and they know exactly who to go to for help. Perhaps other hospitals might consider introducing a similar idea, especially the larger ones where it is difficult for mothers to get to know the staff.

First class — constant help and encouragement to breastfeed.

Very little — found myself helping other women in the ward.

Leaflets, encouragement from the doctors, nurses and the sister in charge. They were most helpful, day or night.

Other advice

Since this chapter is not strictly about the physical mechanism of breastfeeding, only a few aspects have been mentioned here. Do equip yourself in advance with one of the many helpful books on the subject, as these deal with any special problems that might arise, and keep it by you after the baby is born. You can also contact the hospital after you have been discharged, the public health nurse at your local clinic or your GP.

However, two special circumstances are mentioned here as a fair number of women may be affected by one or both during their hospital stay. These are breastfeeding after a Caesarian section and breastfeeding if your baby is in a special care unit.

161

Breastfeeding after a section

Having undergone a section is not a reason in itself to give up the idea of breastfeeding. It is quite possible to feed in these circumstances, though you'll need help and encouragement to begin with. You may not be feeling in very good form — after all, you've had major abdominal surgery — and you may not feel ready to cope with the baby just yet. However, do try to feed the baby as soon as possible to encourage the milk supply.

Also, since you have some degree of discomfort from your scar, you may not be able to adopt the usual sitting position for feeding, at least to begin with. In this case either lie down with the baby beside you and lean towards him (and ask a nurse to move him over when it's time to change sides, if you can't manage for yourself) or, when you're feeling a bit better, cushion the baby on a pillow across your tummy so that he doesn't press on your scar.

If you know that you're going to have a section then you should read as much as possible in advance about breastfeeding in these circumstances. It might also be as well to get in touch with either La Leche League or the Irish Childbirth Trust (or both!) and talk to them about it, and perhaps get hold of their leaflets on feeding in these circumstances. In any case it might be a good idea for all prospective breastfeeding mothers to read a little bit on the subject, just in case an emergency section is done during labour and you have to cope with an unplanned situation.

Breastfeeding and special care units

Some of this advice is repeated in the following chapter, so have a look at that as well. If your baby is in a special care baby unit (SCBU) you can still breastfeed him, though again it may take a lot of determination and help.

Depending on the reason for your baby being in special

care, it may be possible for you to spend most of your time with him and to feed him yourself. For example, if he is in the SCBU simply because he is "small for dates", he may be able to suck just as well as a slightly heavier baby. Other babies may not suckle as strongly or for very long at each feed, but remember that breast milk is the best food for the majority of these babies and try to persevere until his sucking becomes stronger.

If you cannot feed the baby directly because he is attached to various pieces of equipment, you can express your milk and most hospitals will have a hand pump to help you. You can express your milk manually, though there's quite an art to this and it does take time. Some hospitals may also have an electric breast pump, which some women prefer to use. The milk will then be fed to the baby via the tubes leading through his nose and gullet to his stomach.

You may be able to feed him at the breast before you go home, but if the baby has to stay in hospital without you, you may wish to make arrangements either to go in and feed him or to express your milk and deliver it to the hospital. In these circumstances you're going to need lots of moral support and possibly some form of practical support as well, so discuss it with your partner, the sister in charge of the SCBU and the paediatrician. You might also like to contact La Leche League and the Irish Childbirth Trust, simply to find a supportive listener, but they may be able to offer you practical help as well.

In these circumstances, of course, it can be very difficult to keep on feeding the baby yourself, either directly or by using expressed milk. It will depend on a number of factors — how you feel about the importance of continued breastfeeding, the distance you live from hospital and your transport arrangements, your other commitments and so on. These must all be taken into consideration in coming to the decision that is right for you and your baby.

Breastfeeding twins

This is just a brief word about breastfeeding twins. Despite what other people may tell you it is perfectly possible to breastfeed twins, and to do it for several months. The best advice is much the same as for other mothers: read as much as you can about breastfeeding before the babies are born, with special reference to twins, and do get in touch with LLL or the ICT — they have leaflets on the subject.

Working mothers

Another few words must be put in here about mothers who plan to return to work after maternity leave. Some of them feel that there is no point in even starting to breastfeed if they are going to have to switch to a bottle in a few weeks, while others who do breastfeed may come up against some difficulties in weaning the baby onto a bottle when they do have to leave him.

In the former case it must be repeated that every day a baby is breastfed is to his advantage, so if you feed him yourself for the first six weeks or whatever your leave is, you have given him a tremendous start. In the latter case, get in touch with the ICT or LLL *before* you go back to work, and you should also try to get hold of a copy of Anne Price and Nancy Bamford's book on working and breastfeeding (see Appendix 1).

Bottle feeding

Having made the point that breast is best, you may still prefer to bottle feed. It has already been noted that some women just do not like the thought of breastfeeding for various reasons, while others want to share the feeding with their partners, or to feel free to go out occasionally without worrying about feeding the baby. Pro-breastfeeders will probably not agree with these reasons, but the decision must be yours and no-one else's.

If you decide to bottle feed, or if you are going to breastfeed but know that you will want to give the occasional bottle, you should buy all the necessary equipment before the baby is due. You will need several bottles and teats, a measuring jug for adding the correct amount of water (though some bottles come with the ounces already marked on them), a spoon for mixing, a straight-edged knife for levelling the powder, and the sterilising equipment.

You can sterilise the bottles and teats by boiling them in a saucepan but many women prefer to use one of the chemicals available specifically for this purpose. The bottles and teats are simply immersed in cold water to which the chemical has been added. The chemical comes in either liquid or tablet form. It is possible to buy complete sterilising units consisting of a plastic tank which holds all the bottles and teats in the sterilising fluid until you need them. If you use this method, don't rinse the bottles under the tap to wash off any fluid — you are now advised to use the bottles straight from the solution.

In hospital the bottles will come to you ready to use, but these special ones are not available to the general public, so before you go home you should be shown how to mix up the feeds, paying special attention to the amounts of the powder to be used. *Never* use more than the correct amount — making up formula is not like making a pot of tea, so you certainly don't need an extra spoonful — it doesn't do your baby any good and may do him harm, by affecting his kidneys if the feed is too rich and eventually, if you always add a bit, you are giving him extra calories which he does not need and will put on as fat. Fat babies are not healthy babies and can be storing up trouble for later life.

There are a number of different milk formulas available, and different ones are used according to the hospital you're in. Some hospitals give all babies the same formula while in others there is a choice. You can, of course, use whichever formula you want when you get home. Some hospitals are now giving cold bottles straight from the fridge, but you may feel happier giving your baby warm milk.

Whichever formula you use, do be as careful as you can about cleanliness. Used properly, bottle feeding is perfectly adequate, but it can be dangerous and even lethal when proper hygiene isn't possible or isn't observed. So never skimp on the sterilising procedures for bottles, teats and other implements, and always wash your hands carefully before you make up the feeds or touch the teats. Only make up a batch of feeds if you have proper refrigeration facilities — milk is the ideal medium for growing all kinds of bacteria and bottles left outside the fridge will quickly become full of unseen things your baby doesn't want, so throw away any unused formula left in the bottle.

Don't ever give the teat a quick suck to see if the milk is flowing properly — you might just as well have put it in the dustbin with all the germs it will pick up from your mouth — but hold the bottle up and shake it onto your hand (you can also test the temperature this way) or into the sink.

Never leave your baby alone with his bottle propped up. Not only is this highly dangerous — he could choke or get milk into the tubes below the ears, but however rushed you are, your baby needs this time to be close to you.

As with breastfeeding, if you have any problems you can also ring the hospital for help and advice, or contact your public health nurse at the nearest health clinic, or your GP.

When I was going home I was given two prepared feeds complete with teats, etc., which saved a lot of fussing and boiling kettles when I got home.

Useful contacts: Irish Childbirth Trust
La Leche League
Health Education Bureau
Twins Club Association

17

Special Circumstances

It is a sad fact of life that occasionally things may go wrong during pregnancy, during birth or very shortly afterwards. Though nothing can possibly prepare you for what you may feel if this happens to you, it's as well to know in advance that any reactions, whatever they may be, are normal and perfectly understandable.

Miscarriage

Strictly speaking, of course, miscarriage should be considered in the context of pregnancy rather than in this section on the postnatal period, but for the purposes of this book has been included here because you may well find it helpful to read through the rest of the chapter.

Miscarriages can occur at any time during pregnancy. Technically, and in medical terms, a miscarriage (or natural abortion as the professionals may also call it) occurs before the 28th week of pregnancy, and after that it is a stillbirth, but whenever it happens you will feel a sense of loss. Other people may be more sympathetic if the miscarriage occurs in later pregnancy, whereas early miscarriages may be dismissed rather unthinkingly. Even if you are only eight weeks pregnant at the time, you can still feel that you have lost a baby, and people can sometimes be very thoughtless in their remarks. "Surely it's just like having a heavy period"; "You'll be having another one soon" and "Why worry? You've already got one fine healthy child" are a selection of what you might hear, or some variations on them according to your circumstances. These people don't mean to be cruel, but simply haven't understood how you're feeling. You are right to feel your loss and you should grieve over it as long as necessary. Try to talk about your feelings with someone who can respond to you — your partner (for it's his baby too), and possibly with a friend, especially if she's had a miscarriage herself. Women will often say that no-one can understand emotionally what it's like to suffer a miscarriage unless they've had one themselves, and you may find that this is so in your case.

An early miscarriage is often nature's way of simply rejecting a damaged foetus, but if you have a miscarriage later in the pregnancy you should talk to a doctor to find out the cause as it may be something that can be prevented by medical or surgical means in future pregnancies. Similarly, if you have repeated miscarriages, even very early ones, you should seek medical advice to establish the cause and possible treatment.

Although it's easier said than done, don't spend time blaming yourself for what has happened. You most certainly did not cause the miscarriage by running for the bus, or by making love last night, or by having that row with your mother-in-law the other day. As mentioned above, the great majority of miscarriages happen because of a major genetic fault in the foetus and this is nature's way of getting rid of her errors. So allow yourself to mourn for your lost baby, as it's quite natural to feel such grief, and take any necessary medical advice that might apply to future pregnancies.

I felt shattered and could not believe for quite a while that it had happened to me. But to the nurses it was "hard luck".

I was discharged and just told not to get pregnant for three months.

It all happened so suddenly that I didn't even go to hospital. I recovered physically very quickly but emotionally I was a wreck. My GP was quite good but it was a friend who'd been through the same who really helped me. She listened to me, over and over.

Useful contact: The Miscarriage Association

Stillbirth and neonatal death

Stillbirth (occurring after 28 weeks of pregnancy) and neonatal death (the death of a baby shortly after birth) are cruel tragedies. You have carried the baby in your body for nine months (or nearly so), expecting a new life and yet you have to cope with death. Your body reacts like any other mother's after birth — even your breasts fill with milk — and yet you have no living baby to hold in your arms. It is no wonder that in these circumstances you may be unable to cope with your feelings, and it may seem like cold comfort to be told that you will eventually be able to smile again and to go about your daily life normally.

Some babies die in the womb, some die during birth itself, some die within a few minutes or hours of delivery and others survive only for a few days. In any of these cases the obstetrician and/or the paediatrician will talk to you about the death and why it happened. To begin with you may feel anger at the doctors for not saving your baby, or blame yourself in some way for what has happened. These are normal reactions and are nothing to be ashamed of.

Nevertheless, such a death is a very traumatic experience, and mothers who lose a baby before or during birth may feel happier if they can go home from hospital straightaway. The sight of other mothers and babies may be too much to bear at this time, and the hospital should respect your wishes. Alternatively, if it is absolutely necessary to keep you in hospital for medical reasons, you may prefer to be in a room on your own, and the staff should do all they can to accommodate you in this wish. Staff should understand how you feel and will usually do their very best to help you — though occasionally they are at something of a loss to know what to say, and may try to cover up their embarrassment by pretending that nothing unusual has happened. It has now been recognised that the medical staff need training in responding to this situation, and hopefully your attendants will be aware of your emotional needs at this time.

There is an organisation that has been set up to help parents who have lost a baby either through a stillbirth or a neonatal death. This is the Irish Stillbirth and Neonatal Death Society (ISANDS), founded by a group of parents who have suffered this loss themselves. Their literature should be made available to you in hospital, and they are always willing to lend a sympathetic ear to anyone who needs their help. You will need to talk to your partner too, about your tragedy, because he's lost a child as well. Understandably but sadly some women forget this and turn away from their partner, but you do need to share your feelings. Grieving for anyone you have lost is a slow process that takes time, and the death of your baby is no exception.

As with a miscarriage, there will be a few people who can be unthinkingly cruel. They will tell you that you'll soon forget about it, that you'll soon be having another, that your next baby will be a replacement. Try not to take remarks like this to heart. You don't forget a baby who's lived and moved inside you, and he will always be part of your family. Your next baby won't be a replacement — he'll be the child after the one you lost. Often people make these remarks in a kindly spirit, without thinking what they are saying, and part of it is due to pity and embarrassment

171

at having to comment on what's happened. Indeed, you may even find people who know what's happened avoiding you, because they cannot think what to say — again, try not to take their actions to heart.

You will have to make a decision fairly quickly about what happens to your baby. This is not easy when you may be in a state of shock, and you should discuss it with your partner. The hospital can arrange the burial, and in the emotional confusion you may readily agree to this. However, some women have said that later on they began to worry about this — they wondered if their babies had been treated gently and with proper respect, and wished they knew where the baby was buried. Some hospitals have special plots in cemeteries where these babies are buried, so that parents can visit the site, but this is not always the case. It may be better for you and your partner to make the arrangements yourself — perhaps you can talk to a priest or minister at the hospital, or your own clergyman. It is not an easy thing to think about, but in the long run you may be happier knowing exactly what happened to your baby's body, and that you have an individual grave to visit later on.

Prior to this you may wish to see and hold your baby. As many of us are not familiar with death in the way that the Victorians were, we can be unduly frightened at the idea of seeing a dead body. This too is a perfectly natural reaction, and the staff should understand how you feel. Sometimes, though, with the best of intentions, they may try to prevent you from seeing the baby, especially if he was handicapped in some way, but you should persist that you do wish to see him. Ideally your baby will be brought to you wrapped up, so that you can unwrap him if and when you wish. Many women feel that having seen their baby makes a lot of difference in coping with the loss, because they have a picture of him in the mind's eye; they

172

have a memory rather than wondering what he looked like. You may even be able to have his photograph taken so that you will always have something of him to keep and treasure. On the other hand, if you simply don't want to see the baby, then no-one should force you to and your decision must be respected.

There are indeed no easy solutions in the situation of those whose babies die or are seriously ill. It seemed to me cruel to leave someone who had lost her child in a ward full of happy mothers but of course it might have been more depressing to be left entirely alone.

Useful contact: ISANDS

Special care baby units

All maternity hospitals have a special care baby unit (SCBU), though it may be called something else, and some are more extensive than others. They range from fairly basic incubators to the very latest in technological innovations, and you should also be aware that the smaller units may not have a consultant paediatrician working full-time in the hospital, while at the other end of the range, those units with extensive equipment may have several consultants who specialise even further in the care of very young babies. So depending on the unit, if your baby requires specialised nursing after birth, he may receive it in the SCBU there or have to be moved to another hospital where the necessary facilities and staff are available. In the latter case it may be possible for you to go with him, as it is recognised that separation from your baby at this time is very traumatic, on top of all your worries. You should ask if such an arrangement is possible.

Excellent staff — very understanding, sympathetic and caring.

The child was premature and was given excellent care in the paediatric unit.

Many babies are admitted to SCBUs for what might be called fairly minor reasons. Again this will depend on the policy of the particular hospital, but examples might be babies who are small for dates, slightly premature babies, babies weighing less than a certain weight — perhaps under 5½ lbs. — and all babies born by section.

Then of course there are babies born with major handicaps, such as Down's syndrome (mongolism), spina bifida and other neural tube defects, and babies born very prematurely who need intensive care in order to survive. This is discussed in detail further on.

If your baby is admitted to the SCBU for a minor reason but seems to be quite well, ask how long he is likely to remain there. Some babies can be returned to their mothers very quickly as long as there are no complications, and you should let the doctor know that you would like to have the baby with you as soon as possible. You will naturally feel anxious about your baby being in the SCBU, but ask the staff about anything that's worrying you. The vast majority of babies admitted to SCBUs for minor reasons quickly return to their mothers and thereafter develop quite normally.

They didn't tell me beforehand that all babies delivered by forceps have to go to the special care unit. It seems silly to me unless there's another reason as well.

Visiting your baby
Your baby may be taken directly to the SCBU as soon as

174

he's born, before you have a chance to hold him, and in this case you may well feel quite frightened the first time you see him. Small babies look even smaller when they're lying in an incubator, and they look so defenceless when there are tubes and wires attached to them in all sorts of places. It is quite normal to react with tears and feelings of anguish, or helplessness, or guilt, or indeed anything else.

You may also feel unhappy at being physically separated from your baby and at the fact that you cannot cuddle him, even though you realise why he needs the particular treatment. Once you are accustomed to the sight of your baby in his incubator, ask a nurse or doctor to explain exactly what the treatment consists of, and what all the various wires and tubes or bits and pieces are for. You'll probably feel a bit more reassured once you understand what the various things are for.

In some units it is now the policy to assign one particular nurse on each shift to look after each baby or particular group of babies, and this can help if you know that someone in particular is caring for your baby when you are not there — not that he'll be neglected, of course, but it's easier to identify with one special person. It is increasingly the practice to involve parents in the care of their babies as far as possible. This may involve nothing more than sitting beside your baby, but depending on the circumstances of each individual case, you may, after instruction, be able to change him or carry out various other procedures. Even if he cannot be taken out of the incubator, it is now recognised that parents should be encouraged to touch their infant, so that at least you should be able to stroke and caress him through the special porthole openings.

If at all possible you should be able to visit your baby as often as you want and/or to stay beside him when you want. In some units there may be rules about only visiting at set times, but thankfully most staff now realise that mothers (and fathers) and babies are better together, even in such difficult circumstances. In many units it will even be possible for brothers and sisters to visit, as long as they have no colds or other infections.

If, by any chance, you have been separated from your baby because he has been sent to another unit, it may be possible for Polaroid photographs to be taken of him, so that you can see what he looks like. Some units certainly do all they can to keep mother and baby in contact, even if they are physically separated, and this is to be commended.

Feeding

You should discuss the question of feeding with the paediatrician, especially if you had hoped to breastfeed the baby. A small percentage of babies do have to be fed on special diets — these are usually the very premature infants — and in this case you should discuss with the doctor the advisability of expressing your milk in order to keep the supply going until such time as the baby can have your milk. Some babies have to be fed by tube, in which case you should be encouraged to express your milk, while others can be taken out of their incubators for feeding. In this case remember that very small or sick babies will not be able to such strongly or for very long, but persist for as long as you can, because breastmilk is doubly valuable to such babies.

If problems seem really insurmountable, talk to the paediatrician and get in touch with either an Irish Childbirth Trust counsellor or the La Leche League so that you can work out what is best for the baby and for yourself in the circumstances.

I don't know how much mothers are encouraged to visit and

if possible help nurse their sick infants. While it is obviously easier for the nurses to be in complete control I doubt if it is always in the best interest of mother and child.

I stayed in the hospital for three weeks until she was ready to come home. After the initial shock I found the unit staff were marvellous — they let me go in and out whenever I wanted to, and I could feed her on demand after the first few days. In fact, they were almost too supportive — it was quite a wrench to leave all that efficiency behind and realise I had to cope on my own with her at home.

Useful contacts: Irish Childbirth Trust
                  La Leche League

Handicapped babies

These are the babies who need special care because they are suffering from what might be termed major handicaps. You should be told shortly after birth if anything is wrong with your baby — it is now thought preferable to explain to parents exactly why their baby is being admitted to the SCBU. Possible handicaps are too numerous to mention here, but the paediatrician should explain the nature of your baby's handicap and what can be done about it.

You may very well be quite numb when you hear the news. You may feel that you have "failed" in some way. You may feel that something you did during pregnancy was the cause, or you may feel that you've produced a monster. All of these are quite natural reactions, and you shouldn't be ashamed of these feelings.

A paediatrician should be available to talk to you and your partner as often as you want, until you begin to feel that you are coming to grips with an understanding of the particular problem. Depending on the nature of the handicap, literature about it and any support groups may be available in the hospital.

*We suspected when he was born there was something wrong
— nothing obvious, he was a bit quiet and we had a feeling
about it. The doctor came later and said the baby ought to
go for observation in the special unit. He was honest with us.
He said there and then it looked like Down's syndrome. When
it all sank in I said some terrible things to him, but he never
was shocked, or told me to pull myself together. He let me go
on and on. He helped us face what it was going to be like.*

Another reaction may be that you are a bit frightened
of actually seeing your baby, especially if he was taken away
right after delivery. Fear can work on the imagination until
you have built up a dreadful picture, but often the reality
will not be so bad. If the baby can actually be given to you
(rather than being kept in an incubator or attached to some
special equipment) it might be better if the nurse wraps him
up, so that you can explore his body at your own pace,
just as the mother of any other baby would. Even if you
have to see him for the first time when he's still in an
incubator, the paediatrician or nurse will probably stay with
you and talk about the nature of the handicap. However,
if by mischance the baby is very badly deformed, you may
prefer not to see him, but this must be your decision.

Your postnatal stay

You may have been given a room by yourself, or you may
find that you are in a ward where all the other mothers
have their babies with them. How you feel about this
depends entirely on yourself — some mothers would rather
be on their own, while others find the company keeps them
going and stops them from worrying too much. If, for
example, you are in a ward and find you simply can't stand
the sight of other mothers and babies, ask to see the ward
sister, explain your feelings and see what she suggests. Most
staff will understand how you feel and will try to make

alternative arrangements. If a room is not available it may be possible for you to be accommodated in an ante-natal ward (though again this is not always suitable) or in a gynaecological ward where there are no babies.

If you are to go home before your baby is discharged, check what the arrangements are for visiting. Ideally you should have fairly free access to him, and every effort should be made to accommodate you. If there are difficulties, perhaps because of distance or lack of transport, do talk to the sister in charge of the unit and see what she suggests.

Counselling

If your baby suffers from a mental and/or physical handicap, or if he was stillborn or died shortly after birth, you should receive some form of counselling before your next pregnancy, though not everybody does. This can be carried out in a number of ways.

The obstetrician and/or paediatrician should talk to you in hospital, or ask you to meet him if you have left very quickly, about what has happened and to discuss the possible causes. In certain cases you may also be referred to a geneticist, who can enlarge on what has already been explained to you about your baby. It is often possible to work out what the chances are of future pregnancies being similarly affected, and this is something else the geneticist will discuss with you. Armed with this information you and your partner can then decide whether you wish to attempt another pregnancy or not.

If your baby is handicapped you should be referred to one or more of the agencies dealing with the particular handicap. Many of these are run by voluntary helpers and can provide both moral and practical support. Addresses can be obtained from your GP, your public health nurse, your local health board, the Health Education Bureau and the National Social Service Board. (See also Appendix 4.)

179

You should be given as much help and advice as possible about coping with your baby's handicap. Depending on the particular problem you may be referred to a specialist or a hospital department for on-going medical advice. If at any time you feel you are getting out of your depth, do not hesitate to contact your GP, the public health nurse or the organisation dealing with the particular handicap. They are all there to help you and lend a listening ear, so do make use of them. Coping with a baby is a difficult enough job in itself, and one with a handicap may call on all your resources, so don't feel reluctant to ask for help.

Useful contacts: see relevant addresses in Appendix 4
  Health Education Bureau
  National Social Service Board

Sudden infant death

It was thought better to include this section here rather than in the later chapters where it really ought to be, because so much of what is said in the foregoing paragraphs also applies here.

Sudden infant death is more usually spoken of as "cot death" because in the majority of cases parents have put an apparently normal healthy baby to sleep in his cot and have later found him dead for no apparent reason. Despite much recent research no cause has been isolated, though some factors have emerged during these studies. The majority of cot deaths occur between two and four months of age, there is a predominance of males to females and deaths occur more frequently in the winter months. The method of feeding does not seem to matter — at one time it was thought that breastfed babies were at less risk, but this is apparently not so, nor is a premature baby at higher risk. Current research is centering on the fact that very young babies may have problems controlling their breathing systems while asleep.

Obviously if a baby is found dead like this, the occurrence is very traumatic for the parents, and everything that has been said above about the loss of a baby applies here as well. Unfortunately the death of a baby in these circumstances can be even more traumatic than imagined because under the Coroners Act of 1962 the Gardai are obliged to enquire into the cause of the death, and the effect of the arrival of a uniformed gardai at such a time can be most distressing — though all gardai are made aware during their training of the special approach needed for such an enquiry.

The Irish Sudden Infant Death Association (ISIDA) was founded by a mother who lost her son in this way. ISIDA, in conjunction with the Health Education Bureau, publishes a very useful booklet called *Cot Death — the Facts, the Fears, the Future*. They also have "befrienders" — parents who have lost a baby in this way and who will meet and support newly bereaved parents if they so wish — and support groups in several parts of the country, and you should contact them if ever you need to know more about sudden infant death.

Useful contact: ISIDA

18

Single Mothers

We have already looked in Chapter 1 at the services available to single expectant mothers; this chapter looks at the options available after the baby is born. Basically there are two: offering the baby for adoption or keeping him.

Adoption

It must be emphasised that this is only a brief outline of what is a complex procedure and you must, of course, take expert advice. In any case this option will be thoroughly explored with you by those helping you to come to a decision. You can ask for advice and information about adoption at any time during your pregnancy — if you have contacted one of the organisations for single parents they should be able to help you. Alternatively you can approach one or more of the adoption societies to discuss what is involved. A list of these can be obtained from the Adoption Board or the Federation of Services for Unmarried Parents and their Children (FSUPC). Incidentally, the Adoption Board itself does not arrange adoptions; it has an administrative function under the Adoption Acts and makes or refuses adoption orders (see below).

If you decide to offer your baby for adoption you have to wait until the baby is born before you can start the formal proceedings. You can then ask one of the adoption societies to arrange the adoption, or you can ask your health board to do it, or you can do it yourself. In the latter case you must give notice in writing to your health board of the arrangements. You should note that it is illegal for a third party (such as a priest, for example) to arrange an adoption.

The society you have approached will help you decide whether to care for your baby after birth or whether he should go to special accommodation until he is adopted.

To begin with the adoption society will make sure that the mother understands exactly what adoption means. There is in fact a statement known as Form 10 which explains this, and it has to be read and signed by the mother before the society can start to arrange the adoption.

Once the baby is six weeks old the mother can sign the final consent form for adoption. This form is only presented to the mother after a formal application has been made by the prospective adopters, and it has to be signed in the presence of a Commissioner for Oaths. It also describes the permanent effect of the adoption order and sets out the circumstances in which the natural mother can withdraw her consent to the adoption. The mother also has to be interviewed by an "authorised person" who is appointed by the Adoption Board and delegated to carry out this interview on its behalf. In fact the interview consists of the "authorised person" asking the mother a list of questions on a statutory form to ensure that she is giving her free consent to her child's adoption and that she knows her rights in the matter.

Among other things the mother may state her wishes for the religious upbringing of the child, and she must be informed of the religious affiliation of the prospective adopters before she signs the consent form.

Once the consent has been given and Form 10 has been signed, the parents who are adopting the child apply to the Adoption Board for an Adoption Order. Once the Adoption Order is made it is final and the adopters assume all rights to the child. However, it is possible for a mother to change her mind between giving consent and the Adoption Order being made.

The natural mother will be notified by the Adoption Board of the date of the adoption order, unless she has stated in writing that she does not wish to be informed.

Again, it must be emphasised that this is only the very barest outline of the whole procedure, and for further information you should contact either your health board or one of the adoption societies. All your contact with them will be kept completely confidential, so you can approach them for advice and help in confidence.

Barnardo's provide a confidential and independent phone-in service for anyone who has any problems about adoption or who is simply looking for advice. You need not even give your name unless you want to do so. This service operates every Tuesday afternoon from two o'clock until six-thirty and the number to ring is Dublin 960042.

Useful contacts: The Adoption Board
FSUPC
Protestant Adoption Society
Barnardo's
Challenge
Cherish
Children First

Keeping your baby
If you decide to keep your baby you will need as much information, help and support as possible, and you would be well advised (if you have not already done so) to contact one of the organisations specifically dealing with single parents (see Chapter 1 for more details). They can provide you with all the advice you are likely to need, and can also give you the extra emotional support that you may need.

In a book of this sort it would be impossible to include all the relevant and necessary information for single mothers, and in fact, this has already been gathered and published in the FSUPC's *Directory of Services in Ireland for Unmarried Parents and their Children*. This Directory covers the following topics: social work agencies, medical care, financial entitlements (maternity allowances, children's allowance, supplementary allowance, unmarried mother's allowance, tax and maintenance payments), accommodation (pre-natal, post-natal, local authority accommodation, private accommodation and home ownership), adoption (general information and adoption agencies), provision of care for children (day care, day nurseries, playgroups, fostering and residential care) and legal aspects (rights of unmarried parents, registration, affiliation, maintenance, inheritance, wills, illegitimacy, marriage, employment and legal aid). You would be well advised to obtain a copy of this excellent booklet, which can be ordered by post from the FSUPC. The other groups will also prove helpful.

There are also several groups which, while not providing a counselling and information service for new mothers, do provide social contact and long-term support for single parents.

Useful contacts: Alone Parents Association
                  Ally
                  Amie
                  Barnardo's
                  Challenge
                  Cherish
                  FSUPC
                  Gingerbread Ireland
                  Life Ireland
                  Protestant Adoption Society & Single
                  Parent Counselling Service

19

Postnatal Check-up

Before you leave the maternity unit you may be given an appointment to return between six and eight weeks later for your postnatal examination. This time allows your body to return to something like normal and yet it is early enough for contraceptive advice to be given before you can become pregnant again. (However, you should be aware that it's possible to conceive *before* your first period arrives, so you may wish to take some contraceptive precautions as soon as you resume intercourse.) Alternatively you may be told to ring nearer the time for an appointment (this is usually the case with private patients), while some women prefer to attend their GP for the check-up, and some hospitals ask women to do this anyway.

At your check-up the doctor will ask you a number of questions — how long bleeding continued after delivery, if a period has occurred since then, if the site of the episiotomy (if one was done) has healed satisfactorily or if there is any discomfort or pain, especially on intercourse. Should you have any special problems or questions, make a note of them before you go for the appointment, so that you have them ready to discuss at this point — otherwise you may not remember until you're on your way home!

He was still good at the postnatal. He explained what he was doing during the internal and the smear. Nicest of all, because

I had the baby with me, he took the trouble to ask how I was managing at home. He obviously wanted to hear if I was having any problems, even if they weren't strictly his department any more.

Cervical smear tests

The doctor will also give you a physical examination, including an internal check. He will make sure that the uterus and cervix have returned to normal, and he will examine the episiotomy scar. Usually a cervical smear is taken at this time, to detect the presence of pre-cancerous and cancerous cells. This check is extremely important and you should make sure your doctor does one. If he does not, ask him why — there are a few doctors who feel that this is still too early after birth to do this test, and if your doctor is one of these, ask him when you should return. He will use a special instrument to remove a few cells from the surface of the cervix, and while this is being done you can use your relaxation techniques so that you don't tense up. You should find the procedure painless as long as you relax. The cells are placed on a slide which is then sent to a laboratory to be examined. The current practice is that you will only hear anything further about the test if an abnormality shows up, though often all that is revealed is some other minor condition of the cervix.

It is worth noting here that because cancer of the cervix is completely curable if caught early enough, the importance of regular smear testing cannot be emphasised enough. At the moment you are advised to have a test every two years, and you can go to your GP or to one of the clinics provided by the Irish Cancer Society in many areas of the country. Recently a walk-in clinic has been opened at Hume Street Hospital in Dublin — this operates all day every Wednesday, and although they would prefer you to make an appointment, if you happen to be in Dublin and call

187

in, they will try to facilitate you. The number to ring is Dublin 766935.

Contraceptive advice

The postnatal check should also include some discussion and advice about contraception, though the advice varies from hospital to hospital and from doctor to doctor. In some units the full range of contraceptive methods will be explained and made available to you, while in others you may get no practical advice at all. Some hospitals will give advice on "natural" methods only. This is not meant to be a criticism of such methods, but they are not ideal for every woman. In some hospitals a lecture is given every few days in the postnatal wards on the subject of contraception, so that the majority of women receive some advice before they are discharged.

The local GP gives no advice, so unless you know of another doctor you have to go to the family planning clinic.

I asked the doctor at the postnatal exam to check the size of my cap but he told me they don't do that at the hospital and that I would have to go to a family planning clinic. From Greystones it is not very easy to travel to Bray with the baby, the toddler and no babysitter.

Because of my diabetes I have to have more blood tests — I must not become pregnant again before this is done. I cannot have the pill, yet the doctor says I mustn't become pregnant, but doesn't say how I might avoid this. Laughable, isn't it?

Nobody was willing to give me advice and as a result I became pregnant again while breastfeeding.

Billings instruction available locally. I availed of same and had four babies in four years!

188

Having scolded me all through the pregnancy because of my high blood pressure he wrote me a prescription for the pill without asking me if I wanted it. I refused, as I was also breastfeeding, and asked for the cap. As I went out the door he shouted at me never to come back to him.

A sheet of information on natural methods was handed out in hospital. There is no FP service in Wexford. The women's group is campaigning to have one established through the health board, but there's opposition all round.

If you feel that you don't get sufficient advice at your checkup, your GP may be able to help you, though he may not have sufficient training in all methods or he may be unwilling to give advice on moral grounds. Your best alternative is a family planning clinic, but unfortunately these are unevenly scattered throughout the country with most of them being in the big centres of population, but new ones are gradually opening. You can now buy non-medical contraceptives such as condoms and spermicides from the chemist, but they are also legally entitled to refuse to stock such items on the grounds of conscience. Many of the family planning clinics will supply such items by mail order, under plain cover of course.

The choice of contraceptive method will depend on your personal circumstances — age, health, relationship with your partner and the wish (or otherwise) for more children must all be taken into account. The doctor should discuss the various methods in detail with you, but the pros and cons of each method are set out briefly below.

Oral contraceptive or the "pill"
These pills prevent pregnancy by altering the hormonal balance of the body. They are usually taken for 21 days consecutively and the next 7 days are "pill-free", during

which bleeding resembling a period usually occurs. A few brands are taken for 28 days (i.e. with no break between each monthly course) but 7 of the pills are "dummy" tablets so that bleeding also occurs. The pill is practically 100% effective in preventing conception if taken correctly, though it is now known that other drugs taken at the same time can diminish its effect.

It is only available on a doctor's prescription, because there are a number of factors that must be considered. Over the last few years you will probably have heard about a number of reports on the safety of the pill, with some saying that it is perfectly safe and others advising certain women to stop using it. What you and your doctor must do is to consider very carefully whether this is the best contraceptive for you, weighing up the advantages and disadvantages and taking your own personal medical history into account. The pill is certainly very easy to use, as long as you remember to take it correctly, and does not interfere with the spontaneity of sex. On the debit side it can have a number of side effects such as weight gain, nausea, breast tenderness and sometimes a general feeling of not being quite in top form. These side effects are hardly surprising when one considers that very powerful hormones are being used regularly; however, some women may not experience them at all, others may have them temporarily, or may be better switching to a different brand (there are over twenty available in this country) while a very few may not be able to tolerate them at all.

If you suffer from certain conditions you should not use the pill at all — these conditions include heart trouble, high blood pressure, circulatory problems, kidney and liver diseases — but the doctor should always advise you on this. Current research also indicates that women who are over forty and/or who are heavy smokers should not take the pill. If you are breastfeeding it is preferable that you should not take the pill either, as the hormones are excreted in the milk, and it is still not certain what the long-term effects of this on children might be.

In the last few years the "mini-pill" has become increasingly popular with women who for one reason or another were advised not to use the ordinary oral contraceptive. These pills have a lower hormone content that the ones described above and must be taken in a certain sequence. Because of the lower dosage of hormones they are thought to be safer for what might be called the borderline categories of women — women who were not absolutely forbidden the pill but for whom there was a certain increased risk in their use.

There is a slightly higher failure rate with the mini-pills, as they must be taken at a regular time as well as in a certain sequence, and missing one increases the probability of failure. There is also a greater likelihood of "breakthrough bleeding" while you are taking them — this means that you may bleed lightly even though you are still taking the pills, and is due to the fact that the lower amount of hormone does not inhibit the normal functioning of the body as much as the higher dose pills. The mini-pill is thought to be safer for breastfeeding mothers, but you must make up your own mind about this.

Intra-uterine device (IUD)

This is small plastic device which is placed in the uterus. Attached to the device are very thin threads which can be felt in the vagina and which indicate that the IUD is still in place. It is also known as the coil or the loop, and must be fitted by a trained person. Once it has been inserted and checked after a short time, it can be left in place for as long as the doctor thinks advisable.

In theory this form of contraception appears to be a very acceptable alternative to oral contraceptives, as once inserted it needs no further attention, apart from the occasional checking to see it is still in place, and is highly effective. There are, however, a few problems and side-effects.

The IUD can be expelled from the uterus without the woman noticing, and this is more likely during the first three months after insertion and during a period, which is why you must be careful to check for it as instructed. Women sometimes experience heavier and more painful periods than before insertion. A serious problem is that occasionally an IUD will actually perforate the wall of the uterus, causing severe pain and requiring immediate surgery. A less dramatic but equally serious problem is that women with IUDs appear to be more prone to pelvic infections, and that in some cases this has even led to permanent sterility.

Originally it was only possible for women who had had a child to use an IUD, but nowadays women without children may be fitted with one of the newer, smaller devices.

Cap or diaphragm

The cap is a flattish cup made of soft rubber with a firm rim which fits over the cervix (the entrance to the uterus). On its own it not very effective as a contraceptive and should always be used with spermicidal cream or jelly. It must be fitted by a trained person, as there are a number of different sizes, and it must be refitted after birth or if you lose or gain a lot of weight.

The only physical side effect is that occasionally you or your partner may suffer a skin reaction to the cream or jelly, which can be overcome by changing brands. Some women object to the cap because they say it is a bit messy to use, and also because its insertion can interrupt the spontaneity of sex, though it can be put in place up to two hours beforehand. It must be left in place for at least six hours afterwards.

A new development which can be mentioned here is the contraceptive sponge. This is a soft disc-shaped sponge which is used in the same way as the cap, except that it already contains a spermicide. The makers claim that it is effective for 24 hours from insertion and that it is less messy than the conventional cap. The sponge is now available in this country.

Spermicides

This term cover jellies, foams and cream which are meant to be placed at the mouth of the cervix and a special applicator can be used to do this. However, none of them are very effective on their own and should be used in conjunction with either the cap (as above) or condoms (see below). Spermicides can be bought without a prescription from those chemists who stock them.

Another item which could be mentioned here is the C-film. This is a small square of a special kind of thin plastic-like material which has been treated with spermicide and the makers say it can be used by either partner. The woman is supposed to place it as near to the cervix as possible and the man should place it on the tip of the penis; in either case the intention is for body heat to cause the square to become pliable and mould itself to the skin surface, along with the spermicide. Users have found that it is very difficult to unwrap the squares without getting them stuck to their fingers and that the C-films do not get to the right place (for women) or slip in use (for men). They seem to have no advantage, therefore, over the ordinary spermicides.

Condoms

Condoms are also known as sheaths, or are more commonly called by the brand name of Durex, though several other kinds are available. Condoms are made of very thin rubber; they are designed to fit over the erect penis and to collect the seminal fluid in the space at the end. Their use can be combined with the insertion into the vagina of a spermicide (as above) for extra protection and lubrication.

The commonest complaint about condoms is that their use interrupts lovemaking, as they cannot be put on until the penis is fully erect, and they must be removed fairly quickly afterwards to avoid spillage of the semen. They can also occasionally slip off. Some men also complain that even though the rubber used is extremely fine it nevertheless cuts down their sensations during intercourse.

Condoms may now purchased over the counter in chemists' shops; you no longer need a doctor's prescription to buy them.

Natural methods

These are the only methods of birth control that are officially permitted by the Roman Catholic church. There are three main methods of natural birth control: the calendar method, the temperature method and the Billings method of mucus recognition.

a) the calendar method is based on calculating which days in your menstrual cycle are fertile days and therefore unsafe for intercourse, and which are infertile days and therefore safe. This depends on the length and regularity of your menstrual cycle and the dates of your periods, so it varies from woman to woman. You can work it all out just using a calendar, once you have been taught the basic principles, but there are a number of devices which you can buy that will do the calculations for you.

b) the temperature method is based on the fact that a woman's body temperature alters slightly around ovulation in each cycle. Your temperature dips slightly just before ovulation and then rises again afterwards, but you need a special thermometer marked in tenths of a degree to show this. By taking your temperature every morning as soon as you wake up and before you do anything else, and recording the results on a chart, you should be able to pinpoint when ovulation has occurred.

c) now popularly known as the Billings method, the recognition of the mucus consistency is based on the fact that your vaginal mucus is different at certain times in your menstrual cycle e.g. quite thick, shiny, stringy, etc. The theory of this method is that every woman can be taught to recognise the changes in the appearance of her mucus and what these changes mean; by recording these changes on a chart the woman will be able to tell when she is fertile or not.

Many women dislike even the thought of these methods, partly because they need the co-operation of their partner and partly because they require a period of abstinence every month, which naturally inhibits lovemaking and sexual feelings in general. The question of reliability is also another factor which puts many women off these methods. On the other hand, these methods can be useful in teaching a woman about understanding her own body and how it works, but you yourself must decide whether you would be happy with one or a combination of them. All the family planning clinics have information on these methods, and in addition there are a number of agencies specialising in the instruction of natural family planning (see Appendix 3).

Breastfeeding

It might be as well to mention breastfeeding here, as there is a lot of misunderstanding about fertility and nursing mothers. Breastfeeding will usually delay the return of ovulation, and therefore prevent the possibility of conception, but note the use of the word "usually". If you are fully breastfeeding it is unlikely that you will become pregnant; by fully breastfeeding that means feeding every two or three hours during the day and about every four hours during the night. However, some women who are still breastfeeding to this pattern will ovulate and can therefore become pregnant, and as soon as your baby begins to sleep for a long period at night, or if you bottle feed occasionally, or when he starts on solid food, you could become pregnant. Because it can delay the return of ovulation and therefore conception, breastfeeding should be regarded as a spacing method rather than as a fully effective contraceptive method, and you should certainly use another method of contraception to avoid pregnancy.

Coitus interruptus

Also known as withdrawal, this is the name given to the method whereby the man withdraws his penis from the vagina just before he ejaculates. It is a highly unreliable method, firstly because it requires great control on the part of the man to withdraw at this moment, and secondly because some seminal fluid containing sperm may have oozed out prior to withdrawal. Just one drop is enough to cause conception.

Permanent methods

As well as the methods of contraception listed above, there are two further ones which are considered separately because of their permanent nature, namely vasectomy and sterilisation.

— vasectomy

A vasectomy is a short operation, usually done under a local anaesthetic, in which the *vas deferens* or tubes carrying the sperm to the penis are surgically cut and tied. This prevents sperm from reaching the penis but does not affect a man's sexual capacity. He will still produce seminal fluid during intercourse but it will not contain any sperm and therefore conception cannot occur.

It must be noted, though, that even when the operation has been performed it is not immediately effective, as sperm will already have passed the tying point and be stored further on. This store will be used up during intercourse, but the man must return at intervals to produce specimens for a sperm count until it can be shown on two or three occasions that his seminal fluid is free from sperm. This may take anything up to six months after his operation, depending on his sexual activity, and other forms of contraception must be used in the meantime.

It is very important that the man receives adequate counselling before this operation is performed, so that he fully understands what is involved. He should also be reassured that his sexual capacity will not be affected. All the family planning clinics will give advice on the procedure.

— female sterilisation

This operation is performed by cutting, tying or cauterising the fallopian tubes and thus preventing the ovum (egg) from reaching the uterus. There are several different methods of doing this operation, but the particular method used for you should be fully explained to you in counselling sessions and by the medical staff before the operation. Since none of the sexual organs are removed in this operation your hormonal functions are not affected and you will not feel any side-effects in this way.

It is highly important that you receive in-depth counselling before deciding on this permanent method of contraception, and that you fully understand what it will entail. You must also understand that the operation is regarded as being irreversible — in a few cases, in most exceptional circumstances, the tubes have been successfully rejoined, but no doctor would perform the operation with anything less than a permanent condition in mind.

If you do decide that you wish to be sterilised, you will face two further problems. The first is that there are very few places in Ireland where you can actually have the operation done at your own request and unless there is a pressing medical reason, which even then must be scrutinised by a hospital ethics committee. At the moment only one hospital in the country, the Regional in Galway, provides sterilisation on request and only for women within its catchment area. The Victoria in Cork also provides the service, but usually has a waiting list, and there are two private clinics at Celbridge and Clane, both in Co. Kildare. The second problem is that of cost, because unless you happen to live in the Galway region you will have to pay for the operation, so that many women are currently denied this option because they cannot afford it. At the moment it costs about £250 for the operation.

All the family planning clinics will give you advice about this procedure and can provide counselling for you and your partner.

Useful contacts: see addresses in Appendix 3

The baby's check-up
Your baby will also have a check-up about the same time as your postnatal check, though not necessarily on the same day or in the same place — it depends on the practice of each maternity unit. Most maternity hospitals have their own baby clinics but others may ask you to attend at your local health centre or to go to your GP. Private patients may have their babies seen by a consultant paediatrician either in the maternity unit or at a children's hospital. Your baby will be examined just as thoroughly wherever you attend and whoever sees you.

The paediatrician will have a record of the examinations that were made immediately after birth in the maternity hospital, and will compare his findings with these. He will weigh and measure the baby, check that the cord stump has healed properly, listen to the baby's heart and lungs, check the movement of the hips and legs, check the baby's general "tone" and, if the baby is a boy, check that the testicles have descended into the scrotal sac. He will also ask you about feeding and discuss any worries that you might have. If any problems or abnormalities are discovered, you will be referred to the appropriate department or hospital for further investigation or treatment.

20

At Home — The First Year and Beyond

Coming home

The first thing you should do when you get home from hospital with your new baby is nothing! This might sound like most peculiar advice but it is essential that you get as much rest as you can. Obviously you will gradually get back into routine (or lack of it!) but don't come home from hospital and immediately embark on spring-cleaning the house. If at all possible there should be someone else at home with you for the first week or so at least — we do not have statutory paternity leave in this country, but your partner may be able to take some holiday or time off to be at home with you. The provision of home-helps for newly-delivered mothers would be immensely valuable, and many women would be prepared to pay something towards the cost, but at the moment,in the current economic climate, most home-helps are used in providing a priority service for the elderly. However, if you have no-one such as your mother, a sister or someone similar to help you at this time, and if you can possibly afford it, it might be worth thinking about employing someone to come in for a couple of weeks to tidy up and perhaps prepare a meal while you devote your time to the needs of the baby and yourself.

The essential thing is to get as much rest as possible, and to take every opportunity to do so. With a young baby in the house there is no such thing as catching up on your sleep in the sense of making up for lost sleep the next night: you are going to have broken nights for weeks or months so you must rest whenever you can. Many mothers exhaust themselves because they feel they must do as much as they did before the baby was born — that the house must be immaculate, that the meals must be *cordon bleu* and that everything must carry on as previously. Don't fall into this trap! Decide what are the absolutely vital things to do around the house and leave the rest. Relax while you are feeding the baby and at least once a day, when he's asleep, go and lie down — even if you don't sleep, the rest will do you good.

Another thing to do is to let other people do as much as possible — and don't feel guilty about it. For some reason we often feel that it's an admission of failure to ask or let other people do our normal tasks, but especially at a time like this you should take advantage of all the offers you get. If someone will do the shopping, or do some ironing, or even take the baby out in his pram for a walk while you rest or whatever you want to do, then accept! Similarly, if the dust bothers them, let them find a duster and remove it!

Incidentally, you might like to consider using your children's allowance (see below) towards paying someone to come in, perhaps once a week, to clean the house. It can be very easy, especially when you're feeling tired, to let household chores get on top of you, and as soon as you've managed one you find another ten still to be tackled. It can also be very depressing to feel that you never catch up on the work, so it can be good for the morale to have the house tidy even once a week. This is especially true once babies turn into toddlers and older children, and strew their possessions everywhere. Otherwise try to keep at least one room downstairs reasonably tidy so that when an unexpected visitor arrives you don't have to dither on the doorstep wondering whether you can you bear the humiliation of asking them in to witness the chaos!

I feel a woman needs someone with her for the first week anyway and this service should be available for anyone who has no family nearby.

Feel definitely there should be statutory paternity leave to allow fathers to spend more time at home.

Dreadfully tiring. You just have to say to yourself "This is it for the next six months" and adjust your mind — bend with the wind or you'll break.

You and your partner

This is just a brief word about your relationship with your partner. Obviously it is the woman who carries the physical burden of pregnancy, labour and delivery and no-one would deny that she needs and deserves rest and attention for some time afterwards. It is equally obvious that a helpless newborn requires all the attention necessary for his survival and development. That leaves the father. He may well be such a person that he can support his wife emotionally at this time, help her as much as possible round the house and do what he can in helping with the baby; equally, for one reason or another he may not understand these various needs and may even feel jealous.

If at all possible, if you realise that your partner is a bit jealous of all the attention being lavished on you and the baby, talk to him about it, and ask him to share more in caring for the baby. Gone are the days when manhood was undermined for ever by changing a nappy or pushing the pram! If he can get more involved in caring for the baby, not only is some of the pressure taken off you but hopefully he will be happier too.

The other great problem, of course, is the disruption to a couple's sex life. It is probably impossible for anyone who hasn't been through the rigours of motherhood to understand the sheer exhaustion that can build up, not only with the broken nights but the continual demands on your time, what with feeding and looking after the baby and trying to fit everything else in to too few hours. No wonder that bed means sleep and nothing else to many new mothers — the tiredness can be overwhelming, and yet another person demanding something of you is the last thing you need. Also, especially in the early weeks, you may well be sore if you had stitches, and if you have any worries about contraception this can add to your problems.

If you are still sore, tell your partner — perhaps you can find other ways of showing each other affection, or experiment with different positions, and be sure to use lots of lubrication — there are special creams available such as KY jelly. If you're worried about contraception, do something about it — this is definitely a priority job. Refer back to the section on the various methods and go to your doctor or a family planning clinic.

Isolation, depression and stress
Once you come home from hospital and the immediate excitement after the birth has died down, you may feel very flat emotionally, physically tired and wonder if you'll ever be able to cope with your new lifestyle. These reactions are quite normal, and will probably pass as you become adjusted to life with a baby, but some women find that they begin to suffer from what is now recognised as postnatal depression.

Nobody prepared us for the change that would come about in our lives. Although we planned and wanted the baby, for a time when he was just a helpless scrap, needing it seemed constant attention — at times I felt resentful of him and then felt guilty for feeling this way, and if it had been discussed at the classes I would have known that what I was feeling was natural (presumably it is) and I think I would have coped better.

Nerve wracking, total disruption of our lives. It took us a while to adjust to our new responsibility.

Hazy, panic, anxiety, morbid fears with some joyful times interspersed!

I wasn't prepared for problems that cropped up e.g feelings of guilt about not adoring child from start, mild depression, lack of interest in sex, etc.

In our society we tend to be rather ambivalent about motherhood. On one hand our position as mothers is actually enshrined in the Irish Constitution as the supreme role for a woman, and yet on the other hand there isn't too much support given to us in that position. There's very little provision for mothers and children, or thought given to them in the planning of new amenities, and also you'll quite often hear a woman saying almost apologetically "I don't do anything — I've got three children at home". It's not surprising then, that many mothers suffer from doubts about their ability to cope with their role, especially as we feel society expects us to live up to the image of the "good" mother that we see on the fish finger and soap powder adverts — happy and smiling all the time, immaculate hair and make-up, beautifully dressed children, shining house and so on. The reality, for many women, is totally different, especially when you're trying to learn about motherhood with your first baby. Most of us have little or no training in child care, so it's literally a case of trial and error.

Thankfully most mothers and babies muddle along together and survive to tell the tale, but on the way it's not unusual for a fairly high number of women to fall prey to a degree of depression for one reason or another.

I feel there should be a thorough check-up of mothers, for depression especially, at about four months. I do not think that pregnancy comes to an abrupt halt with delivery — physically and emotionally one is still affected for several months.

Horrendous — I was exhausted. No-one tells you how bad it is.

There are many reason for postnatal depression — hormonal imbalance, tiredness, a cranky baby, poor housing conditions, feeding problems, money problems, isolation both physical and mental — the list can go on and on. Or there may not be any obvious cause — you may have the most beautiful house with gleaming surfaces everywhere, plenty of help, a baby who hardly ever cries and feeds well, a car to take you anywhere you want to go — and yet you can still find yourself with depression. Often it's only long afterwards that you realise what that grey patch in your life was when you hear someone else talking about it and you think "But that's exactly how I felt!"

What exactly constitutes postnatal depression? The answer is that there's no set pattern. You may feel perpetually tired, even after a good sleep, and you may find that even washing the breakfast dishes calls for more effort than you can make. You may drift off into periods of blankness, so that you can't recall afterwards what you were doing. You may feel that going out, even to the shop down the road, is too much for you, so you stay in all the time. You may resent the calls your baby makes on you and leave him crying. You may feel violent towards the baby — and then feel guilty afterwards at having had such feelings. The list of symptoms is endless, and you may wonder if you'll ever feel any different.

I feel so cut off, I can't believe I'd feel like this.

I was alright to begin with but after the excitement wore off it all went wrong. I could hardly get out of bed, let alone make it. I'd look at the baby and feel resentment. I hadn't got anything else to do, I just felt part of me was missing.

A major point to remember is that you are not alone in feeling like this. Very often there's a vicious circle in that you feel isolated after the birth, especially with a first baby — you may have stopped work and haven't got any friends in the neighbourhood, or you may feel that with a baby you're restricted in what you can do — and this either causes or adds to your feelings. Once you feel depressed, everything is an effort, so you feel even less like going out. Neither will you admit to this feeling, because to admit depression would be an admission of failure, wouldn't it? Haven't you got a lovely new baby? So why should you be unhappy? So you hide your depression behind a mask of normality, assuring enquirers that everything in the garden is lovely. Well, you may get through it by yourself, but many women could do with some help along the way.

I plucked up my courage to go to the doctor about it, but when I got there I was convinced he'd laugh at me, so I lied and said I'd come about something else instead.

What about your GP? The problem is that many women

see their family doctors as being there to cope with what we can call physical ailments and diseases and would be chary of going to him about depression. Certainly, until quite recently, many doctors, partly because they were overworked and/or didn't know much about postnatal depression or simply dismissed it as female emotional hysteria, would hand over a prescription for tranquilisers or sedatives or anti-depressants. In all fairness, these may work very well for some women in the short term, despite various side-effects, and they may be the answer to your problems. Fortunately all doctors now receive some training in dealing with the emotional illnesses that can beset us, and those who then go on to specialise as family doctors receive more; this means that you are more likely to be listened to sympathetically than was formerly the case, with assurance that you're not going completely mad and reassurance that you're not alone in feeling like this. Doctors are also trained to differentiate between those who need some temporary support and those who may well need longer-term treatment.

However, if what you need is on-going support and reassurance, where can you get this help? You cannot go to the doctor every day, nor can he come and mind the baby for an hour while you have a nap or do the shopping, so what else is there? Ideally we would all have a large circle of family and friends to turn to, but in modern society this isn't always the case. We move around more frequently, so that often we are separated physically from our families and old friends, which means we have to look elsewhere.

If you live in Dublin, Cork or Galway the Irish Childbirth Trust has mother-and-baby groups which meet on a regular basis, sometimes for informal get-togethers in the mornings and sometimes, usually in the evenings, for a talk or discussion on a certain topic. It is not necessary to have attended ICT classes or to belong to the ICT to go to these groups — you can ring the nearest contact for more information about them. You may also find that your local ICT group has someone or some people specialising in postnatal support, which sounds very formal but isn't. It simply means that if you need help or advice you can ring for a chat, or even ask someone to come to see you.

If you have been to ante-natal classes, the members might come together and form a mother-and-baby group (though in big cities this isn't always possible). In other areas there may be groups run on similar lines — look at notice boards to see if they're advertised. The local Social Services Council/Committee may run a mothers' group — again, you can find out about this locally, either from the Council/Committee, the local Community Information Centre if there is one, your local health board, or you could enquire from the National Social Service Board.

It can take a lot of effort to make this kind of contact, but it can break the vicious circle — you are less isolated and you'll learn that other women can feel the same. In fact there's probably another mother feeling exactly the same in your street or round the corner or on your estate. When the public health nurse comes to see you ask her if she's visiting any other new mothers in the immediate area, because she might be able to put you in touch. Don't ever feel shy about telling the nurse how you feel, because she's there to reassure you, not to pass judgement on you, and she will know where the other mothers are or if there's a mothers' group.

If at any point you get really desperate for a sympathetic ear, the Samaritans are always there at the end of the phone. Also, if you ever get to the point where you fear you are going to do physical damage to your baby (or child, as he grows older) you can contact Aid for Parents Under Stress, who run a confidential telephone service to help parents in this position. They will not blame you or censure you:

simply they will lend that important listening ear and try to help you.

To return to postnatal depression itself, there are a couple of excellent books on the subject, so have a look at these if you can. Postnatal depression can strike any woman after any delivery, and though you may be fortunate enough never to suffer from it, you may like to read about it in more detail.

The support I got from friends was very valuable.

For me the letdown was in postnatal care — nobody did care, except the Irish Childbirth Trust and friends.

Useful contacts: Aid for Parents Under Stress
Irish Childbirth Trust
National Housewives' Register
National Social Service Board
Samaritans

Practical help and advice

While in one way you may suffer from a sense of isolation during these early weeks, in another you may be overwhelmed with unsolicited advice about your baby from friends, neighbours, relations, strangers in the supermarket — in fact, any one you do happen to meet, and you may begin to wonder just who is right and who is wrong! However, there are a number of sources to which you can turn for help and advice if and when you need it.

In the first few weeks you can always ring back to the hospital where you had the baby if you have any physical worries about yourself or the child, or if you have any problems with feeding. Your GP will also be able to give you advice: don't be afraid to ask him — you might think you're bothering him with trivia, but more and more doctors now understand and respond to the pressures on first-time mothers. Besides, as any doctor will tell you, they would rather see ninety-nine cases where there's nothing wrong with the child than miss the one who does need some attention and treatment.

Maternity hospital nurses

Depending on where you live and in which hospital you had your baby, a nurse from that unit may call to see you and the baby in the first few days after you get home. Obviously this is quite a localised service, so that only women within a certain geographical catchment area of the hospital will receive such a visit. The nurse will be able to advise you with any feeding or other problems.

Feeding and tiredness

It might be just as well to put in a few words here about feeding and sleeping (for both you and the baby). Feeding, and especially breastfeeding, is probably one of the major problems during the first few weeks. It is not just the feeding itself that is a problem: allied to it is the phenomenon of all those broken nights and resulting tiredness already referred to. This all gets mixed up, so it's not surprising that many new mothers seem to need help at some point with feeding their babies.

While books on baby and child care can be invaluable, many of them seem to gloss over this aspect, and perhaps build up false hopes in new mothers. You are blithely told that yes, in the first few weeks the baby will waken during the night, perhaps a couple of times if you're really unlucky, but that by six or eight weeks he will be sleeping through and a peaceful night will be yours. However, for many, many mothers, the reality is somewhat harsher than this.

If you refer back to the chapter on feeding, you will recall that bottlefed babies usually go longer than breastfed babies between feeds. However, whether he is breast or bottle fed, your baby will certainly need feeding during the night to begin with. In many ways it is easier for those who are breastfeeding, for all you need to do is to pick the baby up (if you keep his basket or cot by the bed it's even easier) and put him to the breast, whereas a bottle either has to be made up or fetched from the fridge, which means getting up out of bed (though your partner may agree to take turns with this task).

Most mothers are prepared to accept this disruption of their sleep patterns in the first few weeks, but trouble may arise when the magic six-week milestone is reached and the baby is not sleeping through the night. Babies, unfortunately, cannot read these books that tell them what they ought to do, and so many of them continue to waken for weeks and months to come. As mothers we may then feel that we are doing something wrong because our baby is not conforming to the pattern we have been led to expect, and the blame may be laid on feeding — and especially breastfeeding. If you actually confess that your baby is still waking during the night at six months you will probably be told that firstly you're spoiling him and secondly you're not feeding him properly, but unless he's actually wasting away before your eyes (in which case you will have realised that something is wrong anyway) ignore these remarks. Many babies waken in the night, and we might be able to accept it more easily if we forgot about a deadline for getting them to sleep through. Obviously it does mean that you may be more tired than usual, but don't jump to the conclusion that it's the feeding that is the cause. See if you can get rest at other times — perhaps going to bed early, and get in touch with La Leche League or the Irish Childbirth Trust, either of whom can give you advice.

Useful contacts: Irish Childbirth Trust
                 La Leche League

The public health nurse

Within a short time of the birth you ought to receive a visit from the public health nurse who is attached to the local health centre. These ladies do sterling work in the community in general, but the system is not really geared to meet the needs of many mothers, especially first-time ones. The notification system, whereby the nurse gets to know that you've had a baby, can be slow and cumbersome and occasionally appears not to function at all, so that some mothers and babies are missed out altogether. Many nurses have large districts to cover, either in terms of distance or numbers of people, and so it may take some time for them to get round to you. Also, while all public health nurses have to have a midwifery qualification this does not necessarily mean that they are all equally interested in mothers and babies as a group. Some of them are excellent dealing with new mothers and babies while others are more likely to treat you as part of the day's routine and no more — and it will be the luck of the draw which kind your particular nurse is. Perhaps the ideal situation would be like that in the U.K. where there are community midwives whose job it is to call on every new mother for at least the first ten days after birth and longer if needs be.

It is nice to have someone look at the baby and say "Yes, he's doing very well" or, "Have such-and-such checked." This visit puts to rest any worries about problems you may notice or things you may miss.

I'd like to have seen her more often — one visit is not enough.

In any case the nurse will have a look at the baby, ask you about any feeding problems, tell you about the local clinic and when to bring the baby for his various vaccinations. Depending on her case load and your needs she will call back at intervals during the baby's first year to see how you are both getting on. If you ever need help or advice you can always ring her and she will either advise you or call round to see you.

She had no children herself and was "going by the book" rather than by experience. She knew amazingly little about breastfeeding — my main problem.

My husband was there and asked her a few questions. I think this irritated her, and she seemed to prefer to address me as if he should not be there. It so happens he looks after the baby when I am working.

I would like to see a good back-up service for mothers when they go home. It would be very reassuring and a good pick-me-up if a nurse (with experience in dealing with new mothers) could call every day to see if there were any problems and to give advice and stem any sort of depression and despair.

Health clinics

The public health nurse will have told you where your nearest clinic is and told you the times of the various services, such as the nurses' clinic, the doctors' clinic and immunisation days. If you have any problems or queries about your child you can attend either at the health clinic or your GP, depending on the urgency of the situation. You can always get in contact with the nurse by ringing the health clinic — a message will be passed on if she is not there.

Immunisations and vaccinations

From his birth you should make sure that your baby receives the various immunisations and vaccinations that are available. None of these are compulsory but you should have your child protected by these vaccines whenever possible. It is important for two reasons: firstly the child himself is protected, and secondly, the more children who are protected against a disease, the less likely the disease is to break out again. When the numbers receiving vaccines fall it means that the whole community is at risk, so all parents should see to it that their children attend at the right time. The public health nurse will tell you exactly when to bring your baby along to the clinic, or you can arrange for your GP to carry out the programme.

The following paragraphs give brief details of the usual immunisations:

— BCG. This is given to babies born in urban areas a few days after birth and protects against tuberculosis (TB), which affects the lungs. A skin test is also done at about twelve years of age to ensure that no further protection is required.

— diphtheria/tetanus/whooping cough. This is usually called the three-in-one, and the combined vaccine is given three times during the first year to ensure maximum protection.

Diphtheria causes breathing problems and can also affect the heart and nervous system. It is now a rare disease but can be fatal.

Tetanus, also known as lockjaw, cannot be spread from person to person like most other diseases but is caused by germs in the soil getting into an open wound. It attacks the nervous system causing painful muscle spasms, especially in the neck and jaw (hence its other name) and can also affect the heart and lungs. It can be fatal.

Whooping cough is also called pertussis. Most people know that the disease is so-called because of the whooping noise made by those suffering from the cough as they try to get their breath. However, it can cause convulsions, ear infections, bronchitis, lung damage and rarely but occasionally brain damage. Pneumonia is another complication. This is an extremely serious disease in young babies and can be fatal.

There has been a fall in the number of children being immunised against whooping cough (and indeed against all childhood diseases, but especially whooping cough). This means that the risk of whooping cough epidemics is becoming greater, and it will be the younger babies who will be at most risk. This decline has occurred because of a controversy in recent years over the effects of the part of the three-in-one vaccine which protects against whooping cough. It is alleged that some children have been brain-damaged by the vaccine, and because of this many parents have decided not to have their children vaccinated. It would appear that most children who have suffered in this way had a severe reaction to the first immunisation but have gone on to have the second and in some cases third doses. There are some children who should not receive the whooping-cough immunisation — epileptics, for example — but your doctor will advise you. If your baby has a severe reaction after the first dose (and again your doctor can advise you on this) you may then prefer to ask that this part is left out for the second and third doses. This combination of diphtheria and tetanus immunisation is usually called the two-in-one. Whatever you decide about the whooping-cough vaccine, you must make sure that your baby is immunised against the other two.

When or shortly after your child starts school, he will be given booster immunisations against tetanus and diphtheria.

— polio. This attacks the central nervous system and can cause paralysis in any part of the body. It can affect breathing and can be fatal. The polio vaccine is given at the same time as the three-in-one or two-in-one and is administered in the form of drops into the mouth. A booster dose is given along with the tetanus and diphtheria boosters when the child starts school.

— measles. This is often thought of as being a simple childish disease, but in fact it can also affect the ears, lungs, joints, nervous system and occasionally the brain. Since October 1985 all children between the ages of fifteen months and five years can be immunised against measles by your GP, free of charge.

— rubella (German measles). This has already been described in Chapter 6 and it is sufficient here to remind you that it is a mild disease except when contracted by a pregnant woman, because of the effects it can have on the unborn baby. All schoolgirls are now routinely offered vaccination against rubella around the age of eleven or twelve.

The Health Education Bureau publishes leaflets on immunisation which are available on request.

Developmental checks

Depending on the manpower available in your local health centre, you may be invited to bring your baby along for checks at various stages. Ideally every child should be seen between six and eight months and then again at about a year. If you are given the opportunity for such a check, do take it, as the doctors can pick up things that may not be obvious to you. At the check the baby will be weighed, examined and then the doctor will carry out various tests in the form of games for hearing, vision and reflexes. If your child is found to be suffering from defective eyesight or hearing, for example, you will then be referred on to an appropriate specialist or department for further examinations and advice.

Children's allowance

You are entitled to claim the children's allowance for each child, and there are no qualifications to be met or means test to undergo.

The allowance is payable from the first day of the month following that in which the child was born, and you must apply within three months of the date of the birth. The current (early 1986) rates of payment are £15.05 per month for each of the first five children in a family and £21.75 per month for the sixth and any additional children.

The claim forms are available at all post offices. For the first child you should use Form AL2 and for subsequent children you need Form AL9. They should be returned to the Department of Social Welfare, Children's Allowance Branch, Oisin House, Dublin 2. Each claim must be accompanied by either a birth or baptismal certificate showing the date of birth.

Some general health advice

These are just a few pointers which may help you, especially with a first baby. You will probably want to have one of the available books on baby and child care, and despite some of their failings, it is very useful and often reassuring to have one in the house to refer to. Most such books cover the care and development of babies and young children, feeding, advice on when to call the doctor, the various childhood diseases, coping with mentally and physically handicapped children, first aid, emergencies and allied topics. Any general bookshop will have a selection of these books, some of which are included in Appendix 1.

Of course, none of these books should take precedence over the expert advice of your family doctor. Never be afraid to ask his advice about your baby — many doctors will have a time each day when you can ring for advice rather than making what might be an unnecessary journey to the surgery, so if you don't already know if this service is available, find out now. In an emergency don't worry what the time is — if your doctor happens to be off-duty or unavailable there will always be a message to let you know where you can get help.

A word of advice about taking a baby or child to the accident and emergency department (which is what casualty departments are called now in many hospitals): especially in urban areas where there are two or more hospitals, a rota may be in operation at night to save the duplication of facilities. You should find out about this in advance, to save time in an emergency, and if you ever do have to make such a visit, you might take a minute to ring and check before you go, as this might save time in the long run.

If your baby does have to be hospitalised, either in an emergency or otherwise, you should be able to stay overnight with him. He will have enough trauma being ill and being in a strange place without being separated from you, so if you wish to be with him, say so. The majority of hospitals would allow you to stay, especially for very young children — some are most encouraging but in others you may have to offer to bring your own sleeping bag. If there are any problems you can get in touch with the Association for the Welfare of Children in Hospital (Ireland) who will be glad to give you any advice or support.

Useful contact: Association for the Welfare of Children in Hospital

The Last Word

Do remember that what is described in these pages is only a general overview of what is happening in our maternity units and other health services today. Things are changing all the time, and while the best has been done to ensure that the information is up to date, it is in the nature of such books that there may have been changes in the services described by the time you read this. Don't forget that it is intended not only as information in itself but also as a source book, so that you know where to go for extra or specialised help, and also to make you think a little bit about what you can do personally to help yourself during pregnancy, birth and afterwards.

There is one last thing that you can do which may help many other mothers in the future. After your baby is born, write to the hospital where you gave birth and tell them what kind of an experience it was, whether it was good, bad or just in the middle. What made it good? Did anything go wrong? Was there anything in particular that you feel could be improved or altered? Were you treated as an intelligent adult? Was your partner made to feel welcome? There's sometimes a gap between theory and practice in a unit, and you should let those in charge know if this is so. By letting them have some feedback, this will help them keep up the good work or decide if changes need to be made, as the case may be.

Address your letter to the Master (for the Coombe,

National Maternity Hospital and the Rotunda in Dublin) or the senior consultant obstetrician everywhere else, and send a copy to the Matron as well. Perhaps people are more inclined to write when it was a bad experience, but if it was a good experience do take the trouble to write as well — all too often the hospitals get all the grumbles and no praise, so give them credit where credit is due!

Incidentally, if you do feel you have some serious cause for complaint, you should write to the Master or senior consultant about it, and if you so wish, ask for an appointment to discuss the matter. The system of dealing with complaints is not terribly satisfactory, and indeed is a matter of concern to both the medical profession and the consumers, as there is no clear-cut procedure to be followed. However, it is probably best to approach the hospital first for explanation and discussion of your complaint before you proceed with any further action.

Finally — and this is addressed to all readers, not just those with complaints to make — you might like to get in touch with one or more of the organisations working in the area of childbirth education and maternity services. Your reports can help them to help other women, by commenting on what is actually happening and by pinpointing what needs to be changed or improved, so try to support them in the work that they do.

Appendix 1

BOOK LIST

Pregnancy and childbirth

Janet Balaskas Active Birth (Unwin, 1983)

Christine Beels The Childbirth Book (Turnstone Press, 1978)

G. S. Brewer The Pregnancy after 30 Workbook (Rodale Press, 1978)

Tom Brewer What every pregnant woman should know: the Truth about Diet and Drugs in Pregnancy (Penguin, 1980)

Gordon Bourne Pregnancy (Pan, 1975)

Danae Brooks Naturebirth (Penguin, 1976)

Tim Chard & Martin Richards Benefits and Hazards of the New Obstetrics (Heinemann, 1977)

Barbara Dale & Johanna Roeber Exercises for Pregnancy (Century, 1982)

Geraldine Lux Flanagan The First Nine Months (Heinemann, 1978)

Ina May Gaskin Spiritual Midwifery (Book Publishing Co., 1978)

Doris Haire Cultural Warping of Childbirth (ICEA, 1972)

Health Education Bureau The Book of the Child (HEB, 1985)

Peter Huntingford Birth Rights: the Parent's Choice (BBC Publications, 1984)

Sally Inch Birthrights — a Parent's Guide to Modern Childbirth (Hutchinson, 1982)

Sheila Kitzinger The Experience of Childbirth (Pelican, 1970)
Birth over 30: How to Plan Ahead and Cope (Sheldon Press, 1982)

The Birth Book (Fontana, 1980)

Giving Birth (Sphere, 1979)

Episiotomy: physical and emotional aspects (National Childbirth Trust, 1981)

Pregnancy and Childbirth (Michael Joseph, 1982)

Frederick Leboyer Birth without Violence (Fontana, 1977)
Catherine Lewis Good Food before Birth (Unwin, 1984)
Ann Loader Pregnancy and Parenthood (OUP, 1980)
Aidan MacFarlane Psychology of Childbirth (Fontana, 1977)
Leonnart Nilsson The Everyday Miracle (Faber, 1973)
Michel Odent Birth Reborn — What Birth Can and Should Be (Souvenir Press, 1984)
Angela Phillips & Nicky Lean Your Body, Your Baby, Your Life (Houghton Mifflin, 1983)
Jill Rakusen & Nick Davidson Out of our Hands: What Technology does to Pregnancy (Pan, 1982)
Grantly Dick Read Childbirth without Fear (Pan, 1969)
Erna Wright The New Childbirth (Tandem, 1968)

Twins
Elizabeth Noble Having Twins (Houghton Mifflin, 1980)
Carola Zentner Twins: the Parents' Survival Guide (Macdonald, 1985)

Caesarian Section
Caesarian Birth — a Handbook for Parents (Cambridge Caesarian Support Group)
Nancy Wainer Cohen & Judith Estner Silent Knife: Caesarian Section and Vaginal Birth after Caesarian (Bergin & Garvey, 1983)
Trisha Duffett-Smith You and Your Caesarean Birth (Sheldon Press, nd)

Home Birth
Sheila Kitzinger Birth at Home (OUP, 1980)
Sheila Kitzinger & John Davis The Place of Birth (OUP, 1979)
M. Monaco & V. Junor The Home Birth Handbook (Souvenir Press, 1984)

Miscarriage and Stillbirth
Susan Borg & Judith Lasker When Pregnancy Fails (RKP, 1983)
Hank Pizer & Christine O'Brien Palinski Coping with a Miscarriage (Jill Norman, 1981)

Postnatal Depression
Katharina Dalton Depression after Childbirth: How to recognise and treat postnatal illness (OUP, 1980)

Vivienne Welburn Postnatal Depression (Fontana, 1980)

Breastfeeding
Sylvia Close Know-how of Breastfeeding (John Wright, 1972)
Marvin Eiger & Sally Olds Complete Book of Breastfeeding
   (Bantan Books, 1972)
Sheila Kitzinger The Experience of Breastfeeding (Pelican, 1979)
Maire Messenger The Breastfeeding Book (Century, 1982)
Ann Price & Nancy Bamford The Breastfeeding Guide for the
   Working Woman (Century, 1984)
Dana Raphael The Tender Gift (Schocken Books, 1976)
Penny & Andrew Stanway Breast is Best (Pan, 1978)

Childcare
John Cobb Babyshock: a Mother's First Five Years (Hutchinson,
   1980)
Michele Cohen & Tina Reid Ourselves and Our Children
   (Penguin, 1981)
Richard & Elizabeth Cook Sugar Off — the Good Tooth Food
   Guide (Great Ouse Press, 1983)
Hugh Jolly Book of Child Care (Sphere, 1981)
Penelope Leach Babyhood (Pelican, 1975)
   Who Cares? A New Deal for Mothers & their Small Children
   (Penguin, 1979)
Ronit Lentin & Geraldine Niland Who's Minding the Children?
   (Arlen House, 1981)
Benjamin Spock Baby and Child Care (Star Books, 1979)
Penny & Andrew Stanway The Baby and Child Book (Pan, 1982)

General health
Derek Llewellyn Jones Everywoman (Faber, 1982)
Sheila Kitzinger Women as Mothers (Fontana, 1978)
   Women's Experience of Sex (Dorling Kindersley, 1983)
Angela Phillips & Jill Rakusen Our Bodies Ourselves (Penguin,
   1978)
Patricia & Michael Quinn Food at its Best (Foresight)
Vivienne Welburn Below the Belt: a guide to gynaecological
   problems (Star, 1982)

Appendix 2

USEFUL ADDRESSES — GENERAL

When writing to the voluntary organisations listed in this section, please enclose a stamp or a stamped self-addressed envelope — postage places a very heavy burden on voluntary groups.

ADAPT (Association for Alone & Deserted Parents), c/o Social Services Council, Henry Street, Limerick. Tel. 061 47111

Adoption Board, 65 Merrion Square, Dublin 2. Tel. 762004

Aid for Parents under Stress, Open Door, Marlborough Street, Dublin 1. Tel. 742066

Ally, c/o Dominican Priory, Upper Dorset Street, Dublin 1. Tel. 740300

Alone Parents Association, 2 Tuckey Street, Cork.

Amie, c/o 13 Saleen Estate, Castlebar, Co. Mayo.

Association for Improvements in the Maternity Services (AIMS), 48 Wyvern, Killiney, Co. Dublin.
The Glen, Faithlegg, Co. Waterford.

Association for the Welfare of Children in Hospital, 11 Hyde Park, Dalkey, Co. Dublin. Tel. 859026

Babylove Ltd., PO Box 187, Kingston upon Thames. Surrey, KT2 5BJ, England.

Ballymun Women's Centre, Basement, Connolly Tower, Ballymun, Dublin 11.

Barnardo's, 244 Harold's Cross Road, Dublin 6. Tel. 977276

Caesarian Contact, 35 Eglinton Road, Donnybrook, Dublin 4.

Caesarian Support Group, 44 Lantree Crescent, Trumpington, Cambridge, CB2 2N2, England.

Challenge, Sion House, Sion Road, Kilkenny. Tel. 056 21653

Cherish, 2 Lower Pembroke Street, Dublin 2. Tel. 682744 Shannon/Clare: 061 61989

Childminders Union, Glebe House, Midleton, Co. Cork.

Children First, 40 Ailesbury Lawn, Dublin 16.

City Centre Creche Co-op, 30 Lower Talbot Street, Dublin 1.

Cobh Women's Group, 1 Kings Terrace, Cobh, Co. Cork.

Coolock Women's Group, c/o Coolock Law Centre, Northside Shopping Centre, Coolock, Dublin 5.

Cork Federation of Women's Organisations, Winnipeg, Ballea Road, Carrigaline, Co. Cork. Tel. 021 372134

CRAWL (Children Require Attention & Want Love), Clooncullane, Strokestown, Co. Roscommon.

CURA, Dublin: 710598
Kilkenny: 056 22739
Cork: 021 501444
Waterford: 051 76452
Sligo: 071 3659
Limerick: 061 318207
Galway: 091 7077
Dundalk: 042 37533
Letterkenny: 074 23037
Athlone 0902 74272

Darndale Women's Group, c/o Coolock Law Centre, Northside Shopping Centre, Coolock, Dublin 5.

Ennis Women's Group, 78 Cahercella Estate, Ennis, Co. Clare.

Federation of Services for Unmarried Parents & their Children (FSUPC), 11 Clonskeagh Road, Dublin 6. Tel. 698351

Foresight, Ashling, Bohernabreena, Co. Dublin. Tel. 513619

Galway Women's Group, 6 Sylvan Avenue, Fairlands, Galway.

Gingerbread Ireland, Top Floor, 12 Wicklow Street, Dublin 2. Tel. 710291

Health Education Bureau, 34 Upper Mount Street, Dublin 2. Tel. 766640/761116

Home Birth Centre of Ireland, 20 Vernon Grove, Rathgar, Dublin 6. Tel. 960750

Irish Childbirth Trust,
64 Carysfort Downs, Blackrock, Co. Dublin. Tel. 888651
38 Ryecroft, Church Road, Bray, Co. Wicklow. Tel. 829190
19 Faiche an Cholaiste, Inis, Co. an Clair. Tel. 065 291120
7 Hartlands Avenue, Glasheen, Cork. Tel. 021 966197
Mill House, Kilmeen, Loughrea, Co. Galway. Tel. 091 41961

Irish Day Nurseries Association, c/o Kinderkare Day Nursery, The Bungalow, Dromartin Tarrace, Dublin 14. Tel. 812748

Irish Foster Care Association, 60 Grangewood, Rathfarnham, Dublin 16. Tel. 944229

Irish Society for the Prevention of Cruelty to Children, (ISPCC), 20 Molesworth Street, Dublin 2. Tel. 760423/4/5

Irish Stillbirth & Neonatal Death Society (ISANDS), 8 Granite Terrace, Inchicore, Dublin 8. Tel. 511292/217717

Irish Sudden Infant Death Association (ISIDA), 34 Sycamore Road, Meadowbrook, Dundrum, Dublin 14. Tel. 983112

Kilkenny Women's Group, c/o SSC, Waterford Road, Kilkenny. Tel 056 21685

La Leche League, PO Box 1280, Raheny, Dublin 5. (also see phone book for local contacts)

Leixlip Women's Group, 5 The Mall, Leixlip, Co. Kildare. Tel. 242862

Life (Ireland), 91 Lower Baggot Street, Dublin 2. Tel. 767676

Limerick Federation of Women's Organisations, 10 Rich Hill Woods, Lisnagry, Limerick. Tel. 061 42444

Loughlinstown Women's Group, 3 Glenavan Park, Ballybrack, Co. Dublin.

Mayo Women's Group, c/o 130 Chestnut Grove, Castlebar, Co. Mayo.

Miscarriage Association, 2 West Vale, Thornhill, Dewsbury, West. Yorkshire, England.

Mothercare by Post, PO Box 145, Watford, Hertfordshire, WD2 5SH, England.

National Association for the Childless & Childfree, 318 Summer Lane, Birmingham B19 3RL, England.

National Childbirth Trust, 9 Queensborough Terrace, Bayswater, London W2 3TB. Tel. 031 221 3833

National Housewives Register, 714 Sarto Rise, Sutton, Dublin 13. Tel. 324422

National Social Service Board, 71 Lower Leeson Street, Dublin 2. Tel. 682422

New Park Community Playgroup, c/o Youth Centre, New Park Close, Co. Kilkenny.

Protestant Adoption Society & Single Parent Counselling, 71 Brighton Road, Rathgar, Dublin 6. Tel. 972659

Samaritans,
66 South William Street, Dublin 2. Tel. 778833
Coach Street, Cork. Tel. 021 21323
2 St. Brendan's Avenue, Woodquay, Galway. Tel. 091 61222
25 Cecil Street, Limerick. Tel 061 42111
13 Beau Street, Waterford. Tel. 051 72114
Ennis: Tel. 065 29777

Self Help for One Parent Families, 52 Grosvenor Road, Rathgar, Dublin 6. Tel. 961666

Tallaght Women's Group, Tallaght Information Office, Dublin County Council, Main Road, Tallaght, Co. Dublin.

Tralee Women's Group, 7 Castle Street, Tralee, Co. Kerry. Tel. 066 36259

Twin Clubs Association, 2 Steele Road, Chiswick, London W4, England.

Voluntary Health Insurance, VHI House, Lower Abbey Street, Dublin 1. Tel. 724499
36 Lower Georges Street, Dun Laoghaire. Tel. 800306
10 Cook Street, Cork. Tel 021 504188
4 Hartstonge Street, Limerick. Tel. 061 45657
Ross House, Victoria Place, Galway. Tel. 091 63715

Wexford Women's Group, Brookville, Newline Road, Wexford.

HEALTH BOARDS

Eastern Health Board, 1 James' Street, Dublin 8. Tel. 537951

Midland Health Board, Arden Road, Tullamore, Co. Offaly. Tel. 0506 21868

Mid Western Health Board, 31/33 Catherine Street, Limerick. Tel. 061 316655

North Eastern Health Board, Kells, Co. Meath.

North Western Health Board, Manorhamilton, Co. Leitrim. Tel. 072 55123

South Eastern Health Board, Lacken, Dublin Road, Kilkenny. Tel. 056 21702

Southern Health Board, Cork Farm Centre, Wilton Road, Cork. Tel. 021 45011

Western Health Board, Merlin Park Regional Hospital, Galway. Tel. 091 51131

Appendix 3

FERTILITY CONTROL AND WOMEN'S HEALTH

Bray Family Planning Clinic, rear Rochalls, Strand Road, Bray, Co. Wicklow. Tel. 860410/828088

Catholic Marriage Advisory Council,
All Hallows College, Grace Park Road, Drumcondra, Dublin 9. Tel. 375649
St. Kevin's, Monastery Road, Clondalkin, Co. Dublin. Tel. 593467
7 Eblana Avenue, Dun Laoghaire. Tel. 801682
35 Harcourt Street, Dublin 2. Tel. 780866
71 Griffin Avenue, Marino, Dublin 3. Tel. 338631
Roselawn Road, Dublin 15. Tel. 212666
265 Templeogue Road, Templeogue, Dublin 16. Tel. 908739
15 Dalymount, Phibsboro, Dublin 7. Tel. 301028

Cork Family Planning Association, 4 Tuckey Street, Grand Parade, Cork. Tel. 021 502906

Dublin Well Woman Centre,
60 Eccles Street, Dublin 7. Tel. 308636/381365
63 Lower Leeson Street, Dublin 2. Tel. 789366

Dungarvan Family Planning Clinic, 11 Wolfe Tone Road, Dungarvan, Co. Waterford. Tel. 058 42617

Ennis Women's Health Centre, 31 Abbey Street, Ennis, Co. Clare.

Family Planning Centre,
10 Merrion Square, Dublin 2. Tel. 767852
17 Main Street, Dundrum, Dublin 14. Tel. 980139
10 Patrick Street, Dun Laoghaire. Tel. 803206

Family Planning Services,
67 Pembroke Road, Dublin 4. Tel. 681108
78a/79 Lower Georges Street, Dun Laoghaire. Tel. 850666

Galway Family Planning Association, Merchant's Road, Galway.
Tel. 091 62092

Galway Women's Health & Information Service, c/o Galway
Social Services Council, Eglinton Street, Galway. Te. 091 63581

Irish Family Planning Association,
15 Mountjoy Square, Dublin 1. Tel. 740723
59 Synge Street, Dublin 8. Tel. 682420
5 Cathal Brugha Street, Dublin 1. Tel. 727276

Limerick Family Planning Association, 4 Mallow Street, Limerick.
Tel. 061 42026

Mayo Natural Family Planning, 37 Roche's Terrace, Ballina, Co.
Mayo.

National Association for the Ovulation Method In Ireland
(NAOMI), 79 Grand Parade, Cork. Tel. 021 22213 Dublin:
Tel. 420825/331300/786156

Navan Family Planning Clinic, Trimgate Street, Navan, Co.
Meath. Tel. 046 21143

Open Line Counselling, 3 Belvedere Place, Dublin 1. Tel.
787160/787664

Ovulation Method Advisory Service, 19 Lower Mount Street,
Dublin 2. Tel. 420825

Waterford Family Planning Clinic, 7 Michael Street, Waterford.

Appendix 4

USEFUL ADDRESSES — CHILDREN WITH SPECIAL NEEDS

Association for the Rights of the Mentally Handicapped,
53 Avondale Lawn, Blackrock, Co. Dublin. Tel. 886523

Asthma Society of Ireland, 24 Anglesea Street, Dublin 2. Tel.
716551

Catholic Institute for the Deaf,
31/32 Richmond Hill, Rathmines, Dublin 6. Tel. 978082

Central Remedial Clinic,
Vernon Avenue, Clontarf, Dublin 3. Tel. 332206

Children's Leukaemia Research Project,
40 Clancy Avenue, Finglas, Dublin 11. Tel. 343986

Cleft Lip & Palate Association,
31 New Park Road, Blackrock, Co. Dublin. Tel. 895480

Coeliac Society of Ireland,
c/o 32 Clyde Road, Ballsbridge, Dublin 4.

Cork Polio & General Aftercare Association,
Bonnington, Montenotte, Cork. Tel. 021 507131

Cystic Fibrosis Association of Ireland,
24 Lower Rathmines Road, Dublin 6. Tel. 962433/962186

Down's Syndrome Association of Ireland,
27 South William Street, Dublin 2. Tel. 793322
St. Jude's, Carrick Road, Boyle, Roscommon. Tel. 079 62511

Down's Syndrome Association of Munster,
Pinewood, Point Road, Crosshaven, Co. Cork. Tel. 021 831571

Dyslexia Association of Ireland,
37 Rathfarnham Park, Dublin 14. Tel. 902214

Foundation for Prevention of Childhood Handicaps,
c/o St. James's Hospital, Dublin 8. Tel. 537951 Ext. 2711

Hyperactive Children's Support Group,
4 Elton Park, Sandycove, Co. Dublin. Tel. 808766 (8 p.m. — 10
p.m.)

Irish Allergy Treatment & Research Association,
PO Box 1067, Churchtown, Dublin 14.

Irish Association for the Blind,
8 North Great Georges Street, Dublin 1. Tel. 742349

Irish Association for Gifted Children (An Oige Threitheach)
c/o Royal Dublin Society, Science Section, Thomas Prior House,
Ballsbridge, Dublin 4. Tel. 944976

Irish Association for Spina Bifida & Hydrocephalus,
Ground Floor, Joseph Plunkett Tower, Ballymun, Dublin 11. Tel.
421222

Irish Deaf Society,
Deaf Community Centre, 31 Richmond Hill, Rathmines, Dublin
6.

Irish Diabetic Association,
Ballyneety House, 56 St. Lawrence's Road, Clontarf, Dublin 3.
Tel. 339577 (Mon. — Wed.)

Irish Epilepsy Association,
249 Crumlin Road, Dublin 12. Tel. 516500/516371

Irish Haemophilia Society,
c/o Union of Voluntary Organisations for the Handicapped, 29
Eaton Square, Monkstown, Co. Dublin.

Irish Handicapped Children's Pilgrimage Trust,
49 Windsor Park, Monkstown, Co. Dublin. Tel. 806032

Irish Heart Foundation,
4 Clyde Road, Ballsbridge, Dublin 4. Tel. 685001

Irish Institute for the Achievement of Human Potential,
Kilnacourt House, Portarlington, Co. Laois. Tel. 0502 23139

Irish Kidney Association,
29 Eaton Square, Monkstown, Co. Dublin. Tel. 802551

Irish Society for Autistic Children,
14 Lower O'Connell Street, Dublin 1. Tel. 744684

Irish Society for Brain Injured Children,
Kilnacourt House, Portarlington, Co. Laois. Tel. 0502 23139

M.S. Ireland (Multiple Sclerosis Society of Ireland),
2 Sandymount Green, Dublin 4. Tel. 694599

Mended Hearts,
15 Coolmine Lawn, Blanchardstown, Co. Dublin. Tel. 214105

Muscular Dystrophy Society of Ireland,
23 Rocwood, Bray Road, Stillorgan, Co. Dublin. Tel. 888967

National Association for Cerebral Palsy,
Sandymount Avenue, Dublin 4. Tel. 695355
(Branches also in Bray, Cork, Dundalk, Kilkenny, Navan, Sligo,
    Waterford).

National Association for the Deaf,
25 Lower Leeson Street, Dublin 2. Tel. 763118

National Association for the Mentally Handicapped of Ireland,
5 Fitzwilliam Place, Dublin 2. Tel. 766035

National Council for the Blind of Ireland,
Armitage House, 10 Lower Hatch Street, Dublin 2. Tel.
    761008/767159

National Eczema Society,
c/o Kilfenora, Gordon Avenue, Foxrock, Dublin 18. Tel. 893243

National League of the Blind of Ireland,
35 Gardiner Place, Dublin 1. Tel. 742792/745827

Polio Fellowship of Ireland,
7 Lower Hatch Street, Dublin 2. Tel. 763245

R.P. Ireland — Fighting Blindness,
67 Silchester Park, Glenageary, Co. Dublin. Tel. 807631 (8 — 10
    p.m. only, Mon. — Fri.)

Saint Michael's House (Association of Parents & Friends of
   Mentally Handicapped Children),
Willowfield Park, Goatstown Dublin 14. Tel. 987033

Western Care Association,
St. Clare's, Station Road, Castlebar, Co. Mayo. Tel. 094 21244

Index

236

238

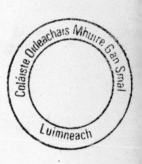